The Lexington Class Carriers

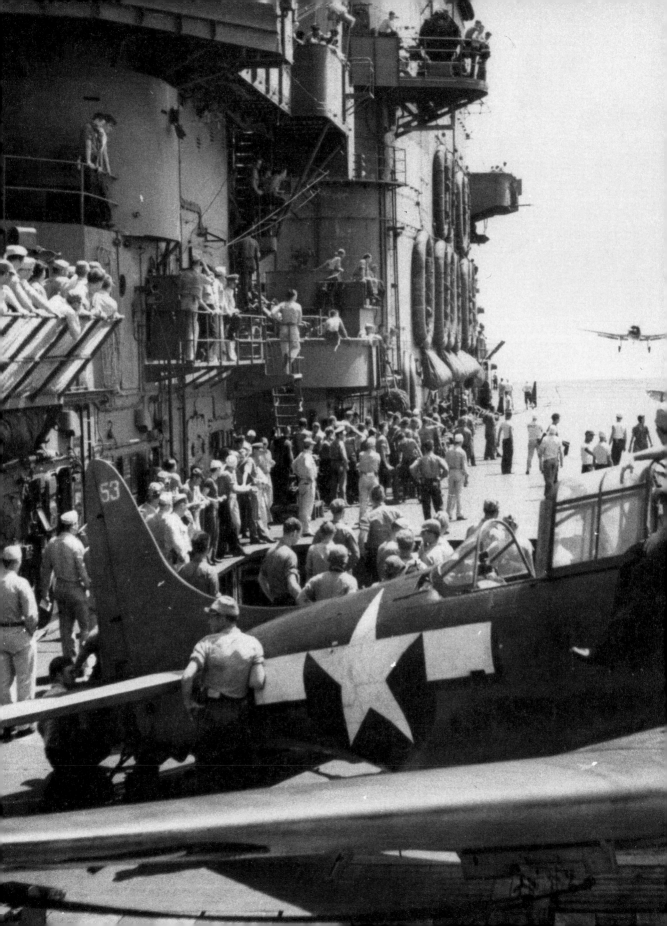

The Lexington Class Carriers

ROBERT C. STERN

NAVAL
INSTITUTE
PRESS

Left: Douglas SBD
Dauntless dive-bombers of
Saratoga's air group,
CVG-12, land after a raid on
Rabaul, November 1943.
Airdales of the 'V' divisions
wait alongside the island to
push taxi-ing aircraft out of
the way and to lend a hand
in case the landing goes
wrong. The remaining
watchers at the higher
levels, collectively known
as 'Vulture's Row', were just
there for the show. (NARA)

To Beth again, because she put up with this process again.

Published and distributed in
the United States of America and Canada by
the Naval Institute Press,
118 Maryland Avenue, Annapolis,
Maryland 21402-5035.

Library of Congress Catalog Card No. 92-62031

ISBN 155750-503-9

Designed and edited by DAG Publications Ltd.
Designed by David Gibbons; layout by Anthony A.
Evans; edited by David Dorrell; camerawork by M&E
Reproductions, North Fambridge, Essex; printed and
bound in Great Britain by The Bath Press, Avon.

Contents

PREFACE

This book tells the story of the emergence of the aircraft-carrier as a naval weapons system by concentrating on two of the earliest and most famous of the type, the 'Lexington'-class aircraft-carriers *Lexington* and *Saratoga*. Obviously, a story as complex as this could be told from any of a number of approaches. This book deliberately chooses one point of view to the exclusion of several others; it is a technical history, describing the 'Lexingtons' as weapons systems. A weapons system, by the modern definition, is a combination of discrete sub-systems that, working together, allow the delivery of weapons against a target at a chosen time and place. By that definition the 'Lexingtons' represented an early example of the type, as they contained within their hulls a myriad of interacting sub-systems, designed to move the ships within range of an enemy, to sense his presence, to strike at his assets or to defend against his retaliation.

The 'Lexingtons' make an ideal subject for this kind of treatment for at least two reasons. First, because their careers spanned the critical early years in the development of the aircraft-carrier, from the initial definition of the type, through the hard test of battle in the Pacific that proved the type and on to the birth of the nuclear age. Second, because in their evolving technologies it is possible to trace the birth and growth of all of the systems that make the aircraft-carrier the still dominant surface combatant.

The story of the evolution of these systems, and the story of the ships in which these systems evolved, is the story of this book.

Acknowledgments Many people have helped me gather the documentary sources and photographs used in this book. Especially important were the staff of the Naval History section at the US National Archives and Records Administration (NARA) in Washington, DC, and Suitland, MD, particularly Richard von Doenhoff and Barry Zerby. Ed Finney of the Naval Historical Center pointed me to some additional photographs that I might otherwise have missed. The staff of the Oral History Collection of the US Naval Institute, particularly Linda O'Doughda, were extremely helpful. Bob Lawson, editor of *The Hook*, was also extremely helpful, particularly in granting permission to quote from Max Leslie's article on *Lexington*'s early days. Arthur Baker provided some key photographs and useful sets of plans. In addition, a number of friends helped with a host of little questions about US Navy habits and customs, and also in putting the book together. That list includes Bob Cressman, Tom Machak and, particularly, Dave Herrling, who, together with my lovely wife Beth, read through the manuscript and came up with a host of helpful suggestions. To those whose names I have omitted, I offer my most sincere apologies. As always, any errors that may be found here are mine alone.

Left: Three whip aerials can be seen on the starboard side forward and one to port in this head-on view of *Saratoga* taken after her last refit, 15 May 1945. All four aerials are in the lowered position. (NARA)

Introduction

The years immediately prior to the First World War saw revolutionary advances in virtually every known technology. Nowhere was this more evident than in naval warfare. In 1850 most naval vessels looked, and were fought, little differently from their counterparts two centuries before. By 1900 steel had replaced wood as the primary structural material, steam had replaced sail as the preferred means of propulsion and the replacement of smooth-bore, muzzle-loading cannon by the breech-loading, quick-firing naval long rifle had increased the effective range of naval combat from a few hundred yards to a few tens of miles. These advances seemed to reach their natural culmination in HMS *Dreadnought* of 1907, which combined heavy armour, high-speed turbine drive and an all-big-gun armament in one hull. By the outbreak of war *Dreadnought* and her successors had effectively made obsolete every capital ship built before 1907.

Technology never stands still or ever, it seems, maintains a steady rate of growth. It is an unfortunate fact that war seems to focus the ingenuity of man in a race to find bigger and more effective weapons. The First World War was no exception to this general trend. When two massive fleets of dreadnoughts met at Jutland in 1916, it was the first and last such encounter. Already still newer technologies were emerging that would make a repetition of Jutland impossible when the world went to war again some twenty years later.

Any future repetition of Jutland was made impossible by the emergence of completely new technologies which saw their first, still primitive, military application in the First World War. Radio, for one, had tremendous implications for naval warfare. If far-flung scouting forces could report instantly over long distances, then the opportunity existed to learn about and exploit an enemy's dispositions as never before. The aeroplane offered even more interesting possibilities as a very fast, albeit short-range, scout, as a spotter and perhaps even as a bomber.

It was the Royal Navy that first saw the implications of these new technologies and took the first halting steps towards taking aircraft to sea. (Actually, both the US and Royal Navies had experimented with aircraft before the war, but those had been isolated experiments with no immediate follow-up.) The British faced a special set of circumstances. German Zeppelins, capable of carrying up to 12 tons of explosives over any English city, created a psychological impact far beyond the mere effect of the bombs they dropped. An effective defence was a political necessity for the British Government. The best defence was to intercept the Zeppelins far out to sea, before they could get near their targets. While the US Navy backed away from its early lead in naval aviation and put its faith in seaplanes, the Royal Navy knew it needed a high-performance fighter with good climb and speed in order to intercept Zeppelins over the North Sea. Contemporary seaplanes had insufficient performance to do the job. What was needed was a small, handy fighter; that meant an aircraft equipped with wheels rather than floats. The British had such an aircraft in the Sopwith Pup. The only problem was range. A small fighter like the Pup had too little endurance to fly from a land base far out over the water, search for, find and intercept a Zeppelin and still have enough fuel left to return to land. Far better to carry the Pup to sea. In 1916 the Royal Navy modified the Isle of Man packet steamer *Vindex* to carry two Pups on a short take-off platform forward. *Vindex* provided no facilities to retrieve the aircraft she launched; of necessity, they had to fly back to land or ditch near a rescue ship. It was a very crude beginning, but it was a beginning.

Notes

The following shorthand for the sources of material used in developing this book has been used to save space in the footnotes:

BuCon	Correspondence (General & Classified), Bureau of Construction & Repair
BuShips	Correspondence (General & Classified), Bureau of Ships
SecNav	Secret & Confidential Correspondence, Secretary of the Navy
I&S	CNO Inspection & Survey Reports
FltProb	Records of US Navy Fleet Problems

GenBd   Correspondence (General &
         Classified), General Board of the Navy
Queen   Queen of the Flat-Tops
Fox   Two-Block Fox
1st   The First Team
BBs   Battleships and Battlecruisers
Proc   *US Naval Institute Proceedings*
Hook   *The Hook*
WI   *Warship International*
Oral   US Naval Institute, Oral History
         Collection
USCVs   US Aircraft-carriers
Color   Color Schemes and Markings US
         Navy Aircraft 1911–1950

Footnotes citing the correspondence files of the Navy are printed in the following format: File, From->To, Date, Title or subject (if any), page number (if any).

Photo Credits

All the photographs reproduced in this book came from a single basic source: the US Navy. (While not unheard of, private photographs were extremely rare in the US Navy during the Second World War and the author has had access to none showing *Lexington* or *Saratoga*.) The US Navy's wartime photographs are stored in two separate record groups at the US National Archives and Records Administration (NARA). Shipyard photographs are in RG 19-N and operational photos are in RG 80.

One person in particular, Arthur Baker, helped by opening up his extensive collection of photographs to me. With the exception of the photographs obtained from him, all photographs used in this book came from NARA.

Classification Markings

A number of the photographs, maps and sketches reproduced in this book retain their original classification markings. The author has been careful to ensure that every photograph and source document, whether directly reproduced, quoted or simply used as research material, has been properly declassified by the US Navy. The fact that some classification markings have survived intact on photographs or charts used in this book is simply a side-effect of the process by which records held at NARA are declassified. When the Navy declassified its Second World War records, it often did so en masse. Rather than marking each page and photograph as declassified – a huge and expensive task – the Navy instructed NARA to mark each item as declassified only

when a request to reproduce that item was received. When reproducing large quantities of documents or photographs, as this author often did, NARA will issue to the researcher a blanket declassification, rather than marking each page or photograph as declassified, thus allowing individual items to be reproduced with the original classification markings intact.

The general declassification authority for the records used by the author is Executive Order 11652, Sect. 3(E) and 5(D) or (E) or Executive Order 12356, Sect. 3.3. The specific authorizations are:

NND 730036   SecNav
NND 863021   GenBd
NND 755023   I&S, BuShips
NND 780063   BuCon

The records of Fleet Problems I through XX (FltProb) were declassified by letter from the Assistant Director of Naval History dated 25 January 1968.

Organization of the US Navy

A brief description of the organization of the US Navy during the period covered by this book may help in understanding the interplay of forces that shaped the design and modification of the 'Lexingtons'. The US Navy was under the political and administrative control of the Department of the Navy, headed by the cabinet-level Secretary of the Navy. The Navy Secretary was a political appointee who may or may not have had any experience or ability to suit him to the position. (A number of distinguished individuals have held the post of Navy Secretary during this century. The list includes Theodore Roosevelt and, in the post of Assistant Secretary during the First World War, his younger cousin Franklin D. Roosevelt.) The Secretary of the Navy was advised by a standing panel of senior admirals known as the General Board of the Navy. Their charter was to respond to specific queries from the Navy Secretary, performing studies and making recommendations as necessary. For example, it was the General Board's responsibility to determine what types and numbers of new ships should be included in the current naval programme; this included the responsibility to develop the general characteristics of new ships.

Operational leadership was provided by the Chief of Naval Operations (CNO), the senior naval post. Below him, the US Navy was organized into bureaux which controlled various aspects of naval development or operation. Those which played a role in the story of the 'Lexingtons' were:

Bureau of Construction & Repair (BuCon) – responsible for the design, construction and maintenance of all naval vessels.

Bureau of Aeronautics (BuAer) – a relative newcomer on the scene at the time the 'Lexingtons' were being designed, responsible for all naval aircraft and an interested party in determining the characteristics of any aircraft-carrier.

Bureau of Engineering (BuEng) – responsible for ship's power systems, originally known as the Bureau of Steam Engineering.

Bureau of Ordnance (BuOrd) – responsible for the weapons deployed on ships.

Bureau of Ships (BuShips) – organized in late 1940 by merging BuCon and BuEng.

Each of these bureaux had its own interests to promote in the development of any ship, particularly in the development of a brand-new type of ship, such as the 'Lexingtons'. BuCon, as the agency that actually designed and built the ships, was the focal point for all of these competing interests. The current organization of the US Navy bears little external resemblance to the bureau system, although the systems commands of today can be traced directly back to the bureaux of the Second World War. Today's Naval Sea Systems Command (NavSea) is the direct descendant of BuShips; similarly, Naval Air Systems Command (NavAir) is the legitimate offspring of BuAer.

During the Second World War the US Navy's tactical command was in the hands of the Commander-in-Chief, US Fleet (CinCUS), who reported to CNO. During most of that conflict the posts of CinCUS and CNO were held by the same man, Admiral Ernest King, who earlier in his career had commanded *Lexington* and, in 1939, had held the post of ComAirBatFor. Reporting to him were the Commanders-in-Chief (CinCs) of the Atlantic and Pacific Fleets, although for part of the period covered by this book, US Pacific Fleet was known as Battle Force. Aircraft-carriers came under the jurisdiction of the Commander Aircraft at fleet level. Thus, the 'Lexingtons' spent most of their career under the tactical control of Commander Aircraft, Battle Force (ComAirBatFor).

1. Design Genesis

Below: *Saratoga*, still a
battlecruiser, under
construction at New York
Shipbuilding Co.'s yard at
Camden, NJ, 1 July 1921.
Construction was
proceeding from the mid-
section of the ship forward
and aft, giving this view into
the bow of the ship. Note
the protective scheme,
consisting of the double
bottom, not yet plated in,
and three vertical rows of
tanks along the side. In the
mid-section, compartments
are completed up to the
third deck level, defining
the central engine rooms
and the flanking boiler
rooms. (NARA)

All successful ship designs come about by a process of give and take, that eventually determines the right set of characteristics for the mission. At best, the process is difficult, as competing interests vie to have desired features included in the final design. The nature of ship design is such that every item included often means that another, equally attractive, item has to be omitted. This process becomes all the more difficult when a new type of ship is being created.

In the US Navy at the time the 'Lexingtons' were conceived, ships were designed to a set of characteristics established by the General Board of the Navy. Among those characteristics were dimensions and displacement that could be exceeded only for the best of reasons. The 'Lexingtons' were designed to a set of constraints defined not only by the General Board's characteristics but also by a displacement limit established by international treaty. This design process and the many factors that influenced the design of the 'Lexingtons' are covered in this chapter.

1.1 Historical Context

The end of the First World War completely recast the strategic picture as seen by the US Navy. As far as the Americans were concerned, there was no question as to why that war had come; in fact, it had been inevitable. A growing commercial rivalry between Great Britain and the expanding German Empire led inevitably to military rivalry. Since the competition was for worldwide access to raw materials and markets, that rivalry found its natural expression as a naval arms race. With equal inevitability, the naval arms race between Britain and Germany led to the First World War, and, because Britain's navy was by far the stronger and her strategic position was far better, the war's outcome appeared to be predictable.

This process was fully explained by the theories of Alfred Thayer Mahan. Mahan was a late-18th century naval theorist and historian most famous for his book, *The Influence of Sea Power upon History*. The essence of Mahan's thesis was that commercial rivalry led inexorably to political conflict.[1] The mechanism was simple: as a nation's commercial power and reach expanded, it developed a merchant marine to carry its goods to foreign markets. An expanded merchant marine required protection, which could only be supplied by an expanded navy. Inevitably, as commercial interests clashed in the quest for markets, so would the navies that protected that commerce. Only the stronger navy could ensure continued access to markets and continued growth.

The US Navy (and others) drank deeply of this heady draught. Mahan's logic demanded the conclusion that the end of the First World War left the world in a far from peaceful state, particularly in the Atlantic. Rising American economic power and overseas interests must challenge Great Britain's position just as directly as Germany's had before the war. According to Mahan, this rivalry must find expression as another naval arms race.

Certainly, the world's naval powers seemed

11

to be following exactly that course. Before America's entry into the First World War, she had already embarked on a massive naval expansion. President Woodrow Wilson announced a plan aimed at building nothing less than the largest navy in the world. His 1916 Programme included no fewer than ten battleships and six battlecruisers, on top of a building programme that had been adding new battleship hulls at the rate of two per year since 1913.[2] Congress largely went along with Wilson's programme, funding four battleships and four battlecruisers in FY 1916, three more battleships and another battlecruiser in FY 1917 and the three remaining battleships and the last battlecruiser in FY 1919.[3] In 1919 Wilson proposed another programme of the same size as that of 1916, although this one was really meant more to put political pressure on Britain at Versailles than as a realistic proposal for continued naval expansion.[4]

The other naval powers had no intention of allowing the USA to gain naval superiority by default. The Japanese had their 8-8 Plan of 1916 which called for the construction of eight new battleships and eight new battlecruisers, but the Japanese, lacking the economic capacity of the USA, were much slower in ordering their new ships. One battleship was ordered in 1916, a second in 1917 and two more were ordered in 1918, together with the first two battlecruisers of the new programme. Great Britain was in the race as well, with some initial advantages and severe long-term disadvantages. The Royal Navy had more truly modern capital ships in the water than any other navy at the end of the First World War, with ten battleships and two battlecruisers (the five 'Queen Elizabeth' and five 'Revenge'-class battleships and two 'Renown'-class battlecruisers), but only one more capital ship (Hood) was under construction and England's economic exhaustion following the war simply did not allow for another full-scale naval arms race. Nevertheless, Parliament reluctantly authorized four new battlecruisers in 1921 and four more battleships were proposed, although not yet funded.

On the American side of the Atlantic, one more element had to be added to any discussion of naval policy. Brigadier General William ('Billy') Mitchell, US Army, intended to play a major role in determining the direction of post-war US defence policy. During the last year of the war, he had commanded an aerial armada of 600 Allied aircraft during the St Mihiel offensive. He came away from the

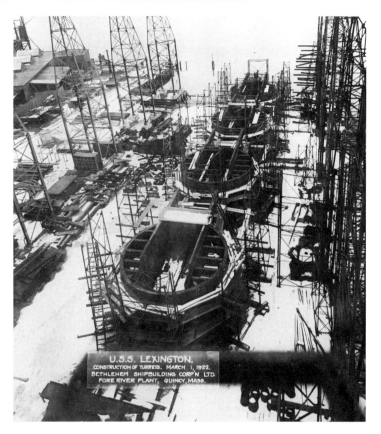

U.S.S. LEXINGTON.
CONSTRUCTION OF TURRETS. MARCH 1, 1922.
BETHLEHEM SHIPBUILDING CORP'N LTD.
FORE RIVER PLANT, QUINCY, MASS.

Above: The four massive barbettes for *Lexington's* 16in main battery, now no longer needed, 1 March 1922. Had she been completed as a battlecruiser, these would have provided armour protection for the shell and powder hoists. (NARA)

experience convinced that air power would revolutionize modern warfare. Back in the USA after the war, he spoke and wrote extensively on this topic, lining up allies in the military and in Congress. His long-range goal was the creation of an independent air force; his short-range target was the destruction of the US Navy.

The Navy's usual claim, when it went before Congress asking for large sums of money for shipbuilding, was that these ships represented the essential first line of defence for the nation. Mitchell repeatedly claimed that his proposed air force could provide that same defence for far less money. After all, the money spent on even one battleship would buy hundreds of contemporary bombers. As is often the case when national policy is debated by ambitious men, the real issues often became obscured in clouds of controversy and boastful claims. In November 1920 the US Navy ran a series of secret tests on the old battleship *Indiana*, part of which involved setting off preset charges in the water alongside the ship to determine the effect of aerial bombing. Mitchell obtained photographs of the tests and leaked them to the press, together with the sensational claim that the Navy wanted to hide the tests so that its ships' vulnerability to aerial bombardment would not be made public. The ensuing public outcry led to the demand that the next series of tests, involving the war prize *Ostfriesland*, include participation by Army aviators. These tests, which ended with the sinking of the target ship, were surrounded by controversy. The Navy claimed that Mitchell broke the rules; Mitchell claimed that he had proved his point, that battleships were obsolete in the face of airpower.[5]

In the end, Mitchell fell from favour, a victim of the outrageousness of his charges and the enemies he had made along the way. Still, there could no question that he had tapped into a vein of public discontent with ever-increasing spending on defence when the world was, on paper at least, at peace and the 'war to end all wars' had just been successfully concluded. Certainly, that same pressure was beginning to be felt by politicians in Washington. In December 1920 Senator William Borah had offered a resolution calling for a tripartite naval disarmament conference, the purpose of which was to be a 50 per cent reduction in capital ship construction. On 29 June 1921, while the *Ostfriesland* tests were under way, the Borah Resolution was passed by the House of Representatives. On 11 July President Harding formally invited Britain, Japan, France and Italy to a disarmament conference to begin in Washington in November.

From this 'stew' of forces and personalities, the 'Lexingtons' emerged. The combined drives to promote airpower and to reduce defence expenditure had the effect of boosting the advocates of carrier aviation in the US Navy. While the Borah Resolution was being debated in Congress, another resolution was introduced calling for the immediate halt in the construction of the six battleships and three battlecruisers then building. As a sop to Mitchell and the Navy, the resolution called for two of the incomplete battlecruisers to be completed as aircraft-carriers.

1. This synopsis of Mahan's main thesis is derived largely from Melhorn's excellent precis in Fox, p22.
2. It is interesting to note that this programme included only one class of ten light cruisers in addition to the sixteen capital ships. (Besides these new 'Omaha'-class cruisers, the US Navy's newest cruisers were the three 'Chester'-class scout cruisers launched in 1907. There were several hundred war-construction destroyers, but these were small and weakly armed by contemporary standards.) When this programme was completed, the US Navy would have had the world's finest battleline protected by inadequate numbers of mostly obsolete scouting and escort forces.
3. Baker, Arthur, *Battlefleets and Diplomacy: Naval Disarmament between the Two World Wars*, WI, No 3, 1989, p247.
4. Hoffman, Major J.T., USMC, *Naval Arms Control Wins*, Proc, July 1991, p35.
5. Zimmerman, Gene T., *More Fiction than Fact - The Sinking of the Ostfriesland*, WI, No 2, 1975, pp142-154.

1.2 Emergence of Naval Aviation

As with any revolutionary technology, the development of practical aviation during the second decade of this century was met in the US Navy by a mixture of strong reactions. A few visionaries were quickly converted into promoters of the new technology; many others baulked at the thought of 'oil on teak'. The US Navy became the first to fund experiments in naval aviation, leading to the launch of an aircraft off the cruiser *Birmingham* on 14 November 1910 and the landing of an aircraft on a temporary flight deck erected on the cruiser *Pennsylvania* on 18 January 1911. The Royal Navy was not far behind with experiments leading to the launch of an aircraft off HMS *Africa* in December 1911. In neither case did these early experiments lead directly to any further developments. Only the pressure of war led the Royal Navy to return to the idea of launching aircraft from a ship.

Aircraft-carrier development, which had been begun so haltingly by the Royal Navy with HMS *Vindex*[1], continued while the US Navy concentrated on the seaplane. By the end of the First World War the Royal Navy had considerable experience with carrying aircraft to sea and had committed itself to an extensive programme of aircraft-carrier development. A report from the Commander-in-Chief, US Fleet (CinCUS) to the Secretary of the Navy dated 15 November 1918 lists no fewer than eight Royal Navy aircraft-carriers in service, or soon to be.[2] *Vindex* had already been retired, replaced by a pair of similar conversions, HMS *Pegasus* and *Nairana*, which had in turn been superseded by later developments and had been relegated to a training role. These two old cruisers had been the next converted after *Vindex* and, like that ship, had only a flying-off deck forward with no facilities for retrieving the aircraft they had launched. HMS *Campania* was an old Cunard liner given a flying-off deck forward like the previous conversions. She was an old ship and the Royal Navy planned to retire her when the war ended, but she was lost in a collision with HMS *Glorious* before that happened. One more ship was converted during the war, and she was destined to become the world's first true aircraft-carrier. HMS *Furious* was designed as a

Saratoga: **Outboard Profile, Starboard (from Booklet of General Plans, BuShips, 112352)**

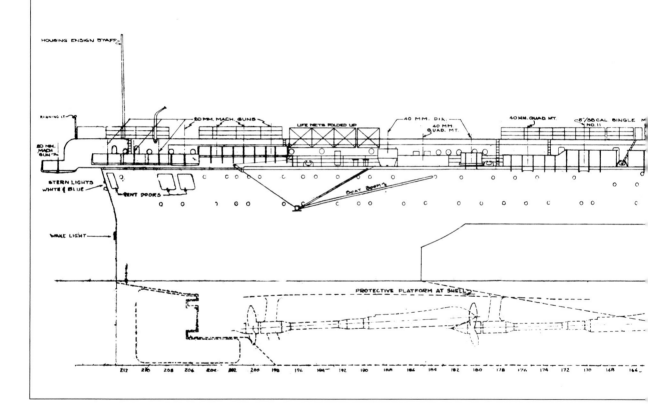

light battlecruiser, a large, fast, lightly armoured ship carrying two 18in guns in single turrets; prior to her planned completion in March 1917, she was taken in hand and given the same type of conversion as the previous ships. Because of her greater speed (32kt), it was hoped that an aircraft could be landed on her forward flying-off platform. The ultimate failure of this scheme led to the decision to make the changes needed to permit the safe retrieval of aircraft. *Furious* was again taken in hand, in November 1917, emerging in March 1918 with a separate flying-

on deck aft. For the moment she still retained her existing superstructure, bridgework, funnel and mast. At the time CinCUS wrote his report, *Furious* was the most modern Royal Navy aircraft-carrier, but three additional, even more capable, ships were noted as being close to completion. HMS *Argus* was in commission, although not yet ready for service. HMS *Hermes* and *Eagle* were nearing completion, the former being the first ship designed from the keel up as an aircraft-carrier. Based on brief experience with *Furious*'s arrangement of separate flying-on

Continued overleaf

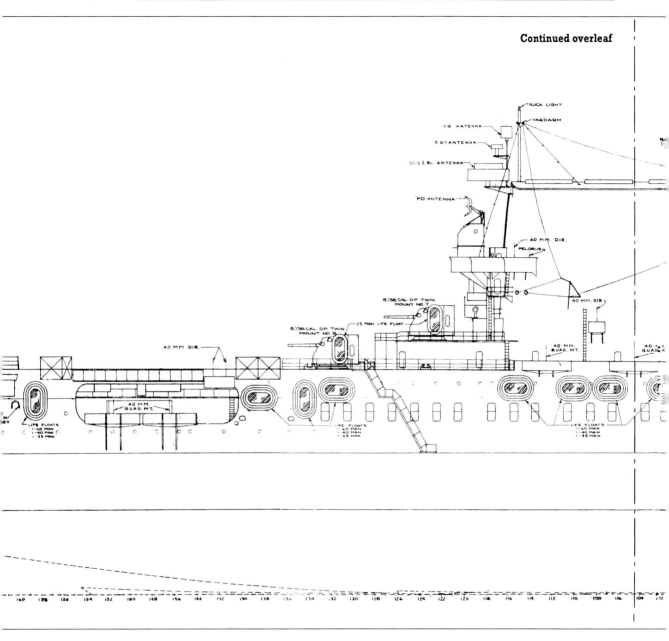

and flying-off decks, which had proved far from satisfactory, all three of the new ships were being completed with full-length flight decks.

The US Navy favoured the seaplane over shipborne wheeled aircraft for a number of very good reasons. Certainly, in the earliest days of naval aviation, there seemed to be little in favour of carrying wheeled aircraft to sea. After all, the particular situation of the Royal Navy, that of combating Zeppelins over the water but still close enough to shore to permit the recovery of ship-launched aircraft on land, was far from

general. Besides interception, naval aircraft would probably also be needed for long-range scouting and short-range battle reconnaissance, perhaps even for an attack role against enemy auxiliaries or light forces. More important, it was considered to be highly unlikely, at least on the American side of the Atlantic or in the Pacific, that these needs would arise conveniently within flying distance of land. Lacking any reliable means of retrieving aircraft (the method used in the 1911 experiment was not considered a practical solution), the seaplane seemed to be

Continued from overleaf

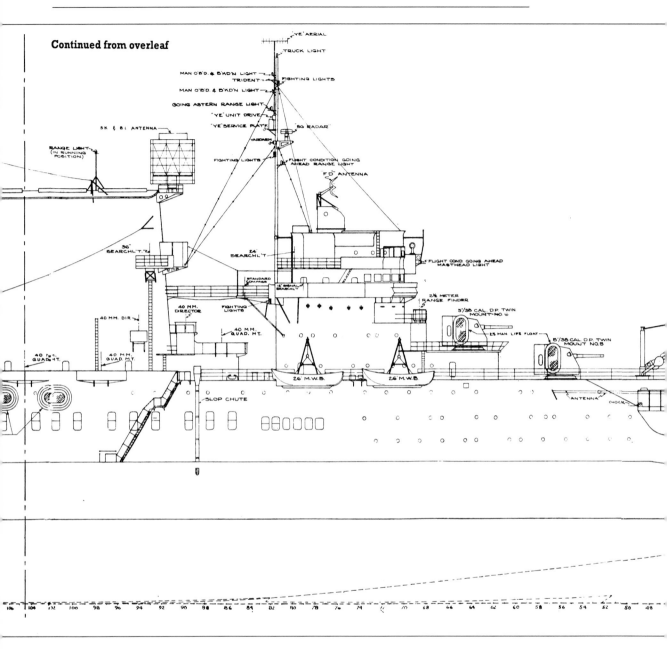

the only practical alternative. Even if that problem could be solved, there seemed to be a host of other arguments against the wheeled naval aircraft, particularly navigation and powerplant reliability. It seemed unlikely, given the instruments available at the time, that an aircraft could fly a hundred or more miles out over the featureless ocean and find its carrier on return, especially since the carrier was unlikely to be in the same spot from which the aircraft launched. More critically, it seemed unlikely that available aircraft engines could

reliably carry an aircraft several hours away from the only safe haven and back again.[3] A seaplane was subject to the same problems, but at least it seemed to reduce the risk to the aircrew. A wheeled aircraft with a dead engine or just lost and out of fuel would have no choice but to ditch, at best a risky prospect; a seaplane could land safely on the water and float indefinitely until rescuers arrived.

There had been a push for the development of an aircraft-carrier for the US Navy as early as 1915, but this was almost immediately upset by

Saratoga: Outboard Profile, Starboard
(from Booklet of General Plans, BuShips, 112352)

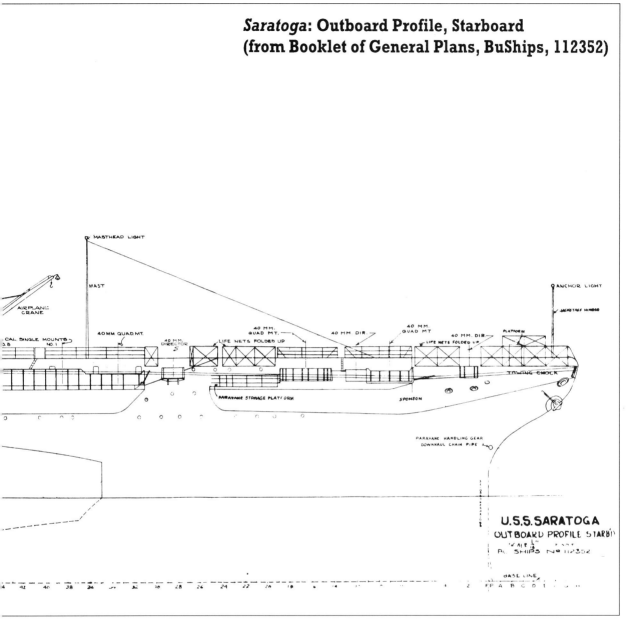

U.S.S. SARATOGA
OUTBOARD PROFILE STARB'D
RU SHIPS N° 112352

the successful test of a catapult, on 5 November 1915, that made practical the launch of seaplanes off otherwise fully capable warships.[4] If a seaplane could be launched at short notice to satisfy a tactical need, then it could be allowed to float around after its mission was completed until there was time to pick it up. The catapult was small enough for any large warship to mount one or two. Nevertheless, the General Board kept trying, without success, for the inclusion in the annual naval programme of funds to build a purpose-built aircraft-carrier.

The reason for the failure to find funding lay as much within the Navy as in Congress. Many of the admirals at the highest levels of the Navy hierarchy, including the then CNO, Admiral William S. Benson, were stubbornly opposed to the idea of an aircraft-carrier.

One way for the conservative leadership of the Navy to blunt the drive for an aircraft-carrier in the fleet was to substitute their vision of an alternative aircraft-carrier, one that carried their kind of aircraft, the seaplane. On 16 July 1918 BuOrd submitted to the CNO a plan for the

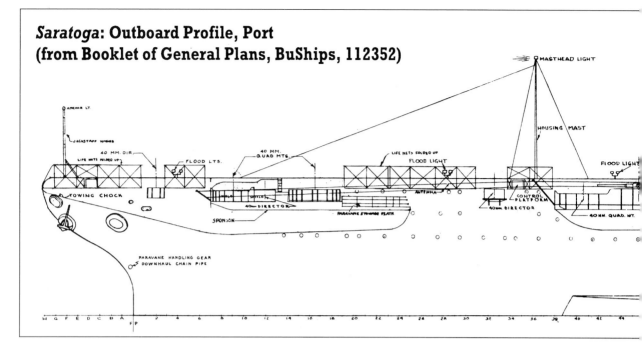

Saratoga: Outboard Profile, Port
(from Booklet of General Plans, BuShips, 112352)

construction of a 'seaplane-carrier'. The arguments in its favour cited in the covering letter indicate that seaplane advocates were equally strong in the opinion that aircraft had to accompany the fleet:

> 'Seaplanes contribute a valuable factor to a fleet for scouting, observation, and long-distance spotting of gun practice in a manner similar to that carried out in land operations and, in order that seaplanes may be available to the fleet, it is necessary that a suitable base or mother-ship from which to operate should be provided. The record of seaplanes on board vessels of the fleet in the past has not been as satisfactory as their importance warrants. The vessels that have carried seaplanes have been deficient because of lack of proper accommodation, due to which seaplanes were often injured if the carrier ship fired a gun.'
> 'The bureau submits herewith its plan for vessels designed solely for the purpose of carrying seaplanes with the fleet believing that it is essential that they operate with the fleet for observation and for offence and defense.'[5]

The proposed vessel was designed with a flat, rectangular deck aft for the stowage and handling of aircraft and a large elevator at the forward end of this deck to lower recovered aircraft to the two hangar decks. Aircraft to be launched would be moved forward in the hangar and raised on a forward elevator into a spacious deckhouse under the bridge, from which they would be launched over the bow by means of a fixed catapult. Fortunately, this idea got no further than did any of the proposals for a more conventional aircraft-carrier.

Despite the considered opinion of many in the Navy that the seaplane answered all its needs, the USA could not ignore developments across the Atlantic. Even if the Navy could find no need for carrier-borne aircraft, the fact that the Royal Navy had aircraft-carriers and that the British, according to Mahanian doctrine, were a potential enemy, forced the US to respond in kind. The logic of an arms race is ruthless: one side cannot let the other gain an advantage, even in a type in which there is little or no interest. In this case, even if seaplanes were perfectly satisfactory in all the roles previously envisaged for naval aircraft, the presence of carrier-borne aircraft on the other side changed all the equations. Seaplanes would always be at a disadvantage when pitted against wheeled fighters. The laws of physics demanded that an aircraft weighed down with large, heavy floats would be slower and less manoeuvrable than another not so encumbered.

A series of tests in March 1919 helped to tip the scales in favour of aircraft-carriers.[6] The battleship *Texas* conducted a firing exercise with the aid of a spotting aircraft. Even though the airborne spotter was a novice, *Texas* was able to obtain accuracy several times better

Continued overleaf

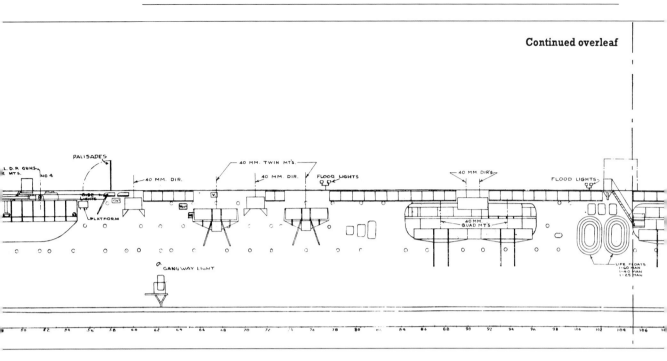

than by ship's spotters alone. These results swayed many of the most stubborn battleship admirals in favour of naval aviation and, by extension, of the aircraft-carrier. The logic of situation was now clear. It was obvious that no navy could win a gun battle in the future without aerial spotting; after all, it had to be assumed that others would perform tests similar in nature to those just concluded with *Texas*. Therefore, it had to be assumed that both sides would have aircraft aloft during a naval battle. If one side (in this case, the US) had seaplanes for spotting while the other side had wheeled fighters, the seaplanes would get shot down and the other side would gain an unanswerable advantage. It had become obvious that command of the air over the battle was an essential prerequisite for command of the sea.

In June 1919 the General Board held yet another round of hearings on the subject of naval aviation. This time they accepted the reality, that Congress had no intention of adding the cost of a purpose-built aircraft-carrier to the already large naval construction budget. They heard from some of the Navy's aviation pioneers:

> '...the people who were interested in this business, Chevalier and Whiting particularly, had figured out we'd better get a carrier in the Navy. So they asked for the *Mount Vernon* — she'd been the *Kronprinzesin Cecilie* — because they wanted a big ship. You need a

large flight deck to operate aircraft from. But they were granted the collier *Jupiter*. She was sent to the navy yard in Norfolk to be converted into a carrier and named the *Langley*.'[7]

The General Board accepted reality and, concluding that any aircraft-carrier, even an imperfect one, was better than none at all, began exploring the list of hulls available for conversion. Since this initial conversion was viewed by all parties as experimental, a good deal of imperfection could be tolerated. Chevalier and Whiting wanted *Mount Vernon* because she was large and fast, but other factors led to consideration of one of the Navy's recently built colliers as a possible source of a hull. The General Board drew up a set of characteristics for the experimental aircraft-carrier conversion.[8] The chosen hull had to be stable and large enough to support a 500ft flight deck, with large holds and hatches and lifting gear already in place. The Navy's colliers fitted this description better than any other candidates. In addition, the aviation community knew these ships well already; the aviation unit commanded by Whiting in France during the First World War had crossed the ocean in the colliers *Jupiter* and *Neptune*.[9]

The General Board officially recommended to the Secretary of the Navy in June 1919 that *Jupiter* (AC3) be taken in hand for conversion to an experimental aircraft-carrier. Even this

Continued from overleaf

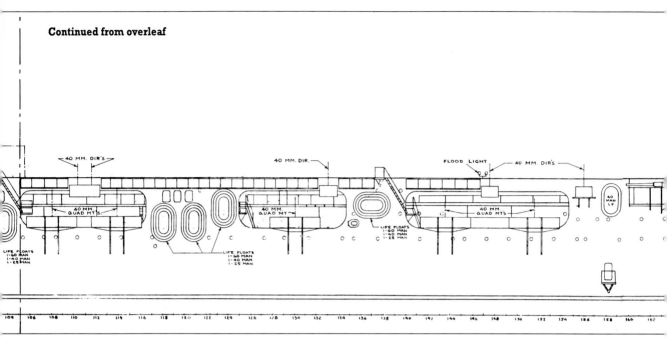

modest request was opposed by Admiral Benson and others who argued that an operational collier was needed more than a small, slow aircraft-carrier, but the Secretary of the Navy overruled Benson and the request went to Congress. It was approved as part of the overall Navy budget on 11 July 1919.

1. Fox, p15. It is a considerable exaggeration to call *Vindex* an aircraft-carrier, but she was the first ship to carry wheeled aircraft to sea for the purpose of engaging in combat. Actually *Vindex* was primarily a seaplane tender. Her entire aft section was given over to conventional seaplane handling; only the bow was reserved for her pair of Sopwith Pups.
2. GenBd, CinCUS -> SecNav(Ops), 15 November 1918, Report on Development of Air Service in British Grand Fleet.
3. Fox, p99. The Army acceptance standard for a water-cooled engine in 1922, the only type then available, was 50 hours' operation without a failure. The Navy believed that this was insufficient to permit safe flight over water by wheeled aircraft.
4. Fox, p16.
5. GenBd, BuOrd -> CNO, 6 July 1918, Seaplane Carrier. Two sketches of the proposed vessel were enclosed.
6. Fox, p37.
7. Oral, Pride Interview No 1, p27. The two officers mentioned by Admiral Pride were Lieutenant Commander Godfrey de Courcelles Chevalier and Commander Kenneth Whiting, two of the Navy's first pilots and advocates of naval aviation. Chevalier was killed in an air crash in 1922; Whiting was *Langley*'s first Executive Officer. *Mount Vernon* was a captured German liner used as a troop transport during the war.
8. Fox, p36.
9. van Deurs, Rear Admiral George, The Aircraft Collier *Langley*, Proc, April 1986 Supplement, p25.

1.3 Design Considerations

Langley

The road from *Langley* to the 'Lexingtons' was far from straight. Certainly, no one expected that *Langley* would be anything more than an experimental vessel. She was too small and too slow to do much more than serve as a proving ground for the men and material that would equip future aircraft-carriers. *Langley*'s specification was as follows:

Langley (CV-1)

Displacement:	11,050 tons (standard)
Length:	542ft 4in
Beam:	65ft 8in
Draught:	18ft 8in (standard)
Speed:	15kt
Range (nm/kt):	12,260/10
Armament:	4 x 5in/51
Aircraft:	33

Her conversion from collier to aircraft-carrier proved to be straightforward. The existing set of kingposts supporting her coal-handling gear became part of the structure of her flight deck. This was a simple platform deck, basically rectangular in shape. It was a continuous flush deck, combining flying-on and flying-off areas. No permanent structures protruded above flight deck level; a pair of collapsible masts and one (later two) folding funnels could be lowered to permit unhindered flying operations. All aircraft

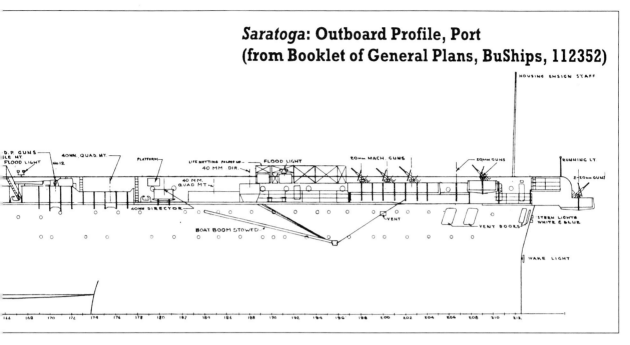

Saratoga: Outboard Profile, Port
(from Booklet of General Plans, BuShips, 112352)

handling was done in the open hangar space between the original main deck and the new flight deck. A single amidships elevator transported aircraft between the flight deck and this hangar area. A fore-and-aft gantry crane lifted dismantled aircraft from *Langley*'s holds for assembly and service in the hangar area. Four of her original six holds were used for storing dismantled aircraft, one was given over to aviation fuel and one was occupied by the elevator machinery.

Perhaps *Langley*'s most interesting feature was her turbo-electric propulsion system. When was launched in 1912, she was the first ship in the US Navy equipped with this propulsion system. It featured conventional steam boilers (*Langley* had three) which powered turbines connected directly to electrical generators. These in turn drove a set of electric motors connected to the propeller shafts (*Langley* had two). It was heavier and took up more space than a conventional turbine system, but it had a number of advantages. It was in theory more resistant to battle damage since the flooding of a boiler room or machinery room need not knock out propulsion on that side of the ship. Electricity could be shunted from side to side in a ship far more easily than steam. Also, and of particular value for an aircraft-carrier, it allowed a ship to make the same speed backwards as forwards. *Langley*'s greatest problem was that speed, forwards or backwards, was too slow.

Langley's numerous limitations made it clear that she could not seriously be considered an operational aircraft-carrier. According to Captain Thomas Craven, the US Navy's Director of Aviation, *Langley* would be useful but far from sufficient:

'There can be no question as to the usefulness of the *Langley* as an airplanecarrier. Though slow, the ship can always be employed as an Aviation base, for the conveyance of numbers of airplanes into an area in which operations are to be conducted, or to operate with slow moving units of the Fleet. The lessons which we must learn cannot be completely taught with one slow craft of the *Langley* type...In addition, and in order to prepare for the strategical and tactical employment of the powerful and fast units which are soon to join the active Fleets, we should now take the steps necessary for procuring a plane carrier suitable for employment with the fast wing, which cannot, without aviation, exercise its full strength.'[1]

The Search for Hulls to Convert

So it was obvious that the Navy could not relax after funding for *Langley*'s conversion had been approved. Almost immediately thought turned to how to go about obtaining one or more fully operational aircraft-carriers. While never abandoning the hope that Congress could be convinced to fund a purpose-built aircraft-carrier, the General Board began its quest for more carrier decks by looking at what hulls

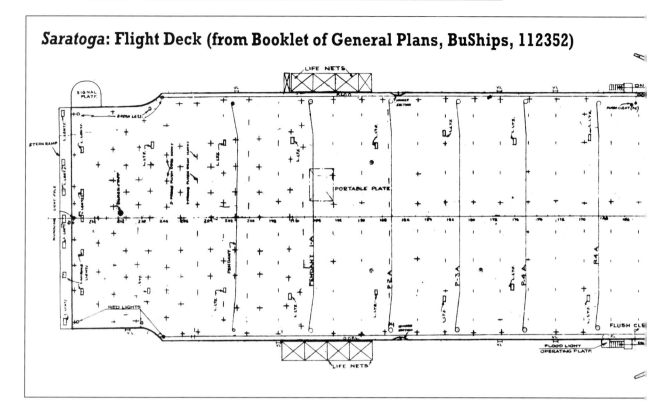

Saratoga: Flight Deck (from Booklet of General Plans, BuShips, 112352)

might be available for conversion.

There were several large German liners which had been interned during the war and for which the Navy had little further use. The idea of converting these old ships had been looked at before by the General Board and rejected as being less practical than the conversion of *Jupiter*. When the idea was raised again in late 1920, it was not from within the Navy but rather by the Navy's persistent opponent, Billy Mitchell. In the newspapers and before Congress, Mitchell proposed the conversion of three liners, *Von Steuben*, *Agamemnon* and *Leviathan*, into three aircraft-carriers, each dedicated to a different kind of aircraft – fighter, bomber and attack.[2] He proposed that they form a separate naval squadron, not under fleet command. This independence from Navy control was to be ensured by the fact that funding for the conversions and for the aircraft that flew off their decks would be from the Army's budget.

Not surprisingly, the Navy's reaction was outrage, every bit as much at how Mitchell was going about making his proposals as at their contents. However, it was by rational point-by-point assault on the practical aspects of the proposal that the Navy was able to deflect

Mitchell's bid for Army ownership of naval aviation.[3]

'Passenger vessels, such as those mentioned, do not lend themselves for conversion to satisfactory airplane carriers as a large portion of the ship must be cut down and new structure built so as to provide stowage spaces for the airplanes and space for elevators [lifts] to bring them up on deck and to provide an entirely flush deck above everything. The ex-German ships named have enormous upper works and a large portion of the ship is taken up with the machinery and boiler spaces, uptakes, etc. Also these vessels are coal-burning which makes it a serious problem to devise means for disposing elsewhere of large volumes of smoke...

'A very serious defect with the German passenger ships lies in the fact that they are deficient in protection against bombs, mines and torpedoes and their construction is such that adequate protection could not be afforded the ships either above the water or under water...

'It will be noted that the reports in the papers to recondition the *Leviathan* for passenger service would cost about $10,000,000. From this it is easy to see what an enormous cost would be involved to largely rebuild the vessel into an airplane carrier,

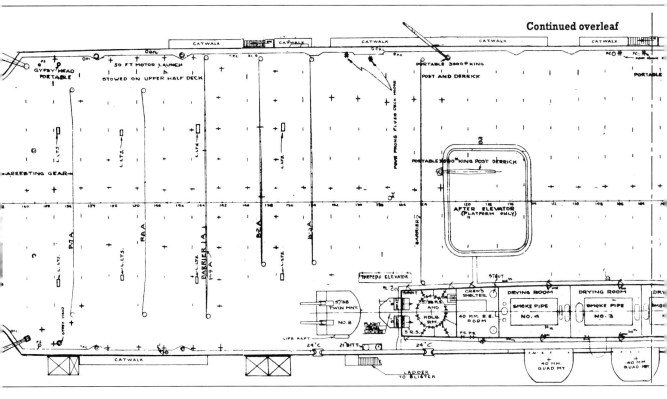

Continued overleaf

which even then would be defective in vital protection. Similar remarks apply to the other two.'[4]

Having convinced Congress that the German liners were unsuitable for conversion, the Navy then had to look elsewhere for suitable hulls. The next candidate to be considered was the class of ten scout cruisers (also known as light cruisers) then under construction. The memorandum previously cited from Captain Craven further stated (in 1920):

> 'The suggestion to convert one or more of the scout cruisers as a carrier is offered with the view that possibly a way may be found through which this can be done, as it would seem to be the only practicable method by which we could now acquire ships.'[5]

In a set of specifications sent from BuCon to the Secretary of the Navy on 12 November 1920, the bureau concluded that a small but serviceable aircraft-carrier could be made out of an 'Omaha'-class cruiser. The specifications were reported as follows:

Converted Scout Cruiser
Displacement: 9,500 tons (normal)

Length:	555ft 6in
Beam:	55ft 6in
Draught:	17ft 6in (normal)
Speed:	31kt
Range (nm/kt):	7,000/10
Armament:	4 x 6in, 4 x 3in, 2 twin torpedo tubes
Aircraft:	18 (12 x VF, 6 x VT)

The bureau reminded the Secretary that construction was continuing on the 'Omahas' and that the longer a decision to convert one or more of these hulls was delayed, the more expensive the conversion would be.[6]

Despite the bureau's relatively positive conclusion concerning the proposed scout cruiser conversion, the General Board saw the basic flaw in the proposal: namely that a converted scout cruiser would not be much better than *Langley*. It would have been twice as fast but no bigger than the converted collier. The resulting ship would still be far from a fully capable aircraft-carrier:

> 'It seems to the General Board that for experimental use little could be gained commensurate with the sacrifice of a serviceable scout...As combatant ships for service with the fleet, these cruisers would be,

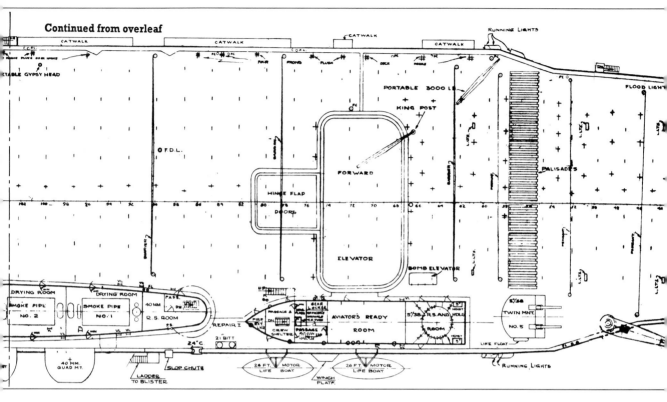

Continued from overleaf

if converted, merely makeshift vessels...
Instead of a good surface scout cruiser we
would have an inferior airplane carrier... The
General Board recommends that none of the
scout cruisers now building be converted to
airplane carriers.[7]

The 1922 Building Programme
While this discussion of candidate hulls for
conversion was going on, the General Board
continued attempting to define the
characteristics of the ideal aircraft-carrier, just
in case Congress could be convinced to pay for
one. For the 1922 Building Programme, the
General Board was thinking in terms of a large,
fast ship with protection on the scale of a
battlecruiser and armament capable of holding
off a light cruiser. The process of defining the
specific characteristics of the aircraft-carrier to
be proposed to Congress began with a request
to BuCon for a draft set of specifications for
discussion. BuCon responded on 6 November
1920 with the following specifications:

1922 Programme Aircraft-carrier
(6 November 1920)[8]
Displacement: 25,000 tons (normal)
Length: 660ft
Beam: 69ft

Draught: 25ft (normal)
Speed: 30kt
Range (nm/kt): 10,000/10
Armament: 16 x 6in plus AA guns,
2 twin torpedo tubes
Aircraft: 72

The flight deck was to be 650ft x 80ft. It was to
have been a flush deck, like *Langley's*, with no
permanent obstructions to flying operations. To
maximize flight deck width, it was intended to
hinge all funnels and masts so that they could be
swung outboard. The plan called for two aircraft
elevators. Armament was to be 6in and 1pdr AA
guns, arranged so that four guns of each calibre
could bear in any direction, and a pair of twin
torpedo tubes, one on each side. Her air group
was to be 72 aircraft, although only a third of
these would be assembled and ready for flight
at any one time. The rest would be stowed
partly dismantled, ready for rapid assembly and
preparation. A 5in armour belt was to run from
an armoured deck of 2½-in thickness to 6ft
below the deep load waterline. Displacement
was to be the smallest possible that could be
wrapped around the other features.

The November 1920 specifications served as
the basis for General Board hearings on

Saratoga: Flight Deck
(from Booklet of General Plans, BuShips, 112352)

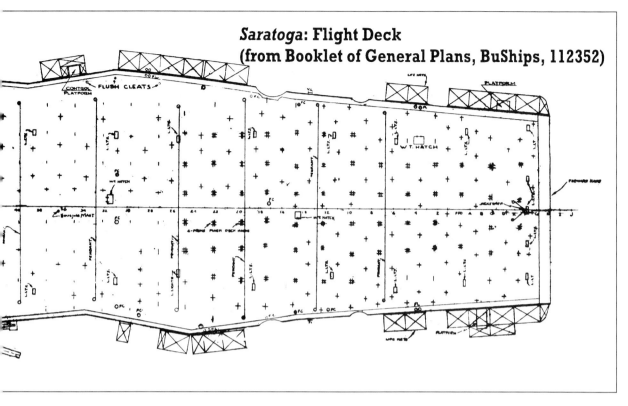

aircraft-carrier characteristics held at the end of the year. By the time the Board was ready to report its recommendations to the Navy Secretary on 24 February 1921, BuCon's original proposal had evolved considerably. The aircraft-carrier now being called for was significantly larger:

1922 Programme Aircraft-carrier
(24 February 1921)[9]

Displacement:	35,000 tons (normal)
Length:	800ft
Beam:	n/a
Draught:	less than 32ft (normal)
Speed:	34kt
Range (nm/kt):	10,000/10
Armament:	12 x 6in, 12 x 5in, 2 twin torpedo tubes
Aircraft:	n/a

This ship was compared with the smaller design offered the previous November:

'The Bureau of Construction is considering two tentative designs for comparison and study, one of about 25,000 tons and about 30 knots. The other of about 35,000 tons and about 35 knots speed.

'The advantages of the 35,000-ton ship are:

1st, large landing deck, 800ft by 100ft; 2nd, great speed; 3rd, steady platform due to large displacement; and 4th, ample stowage space. The disadvantages are cost and time of construction.

'Since Naval Aviation desires the largest deck and the highest speed for immediate experimental development, to accept any speed, landing area or steadiness of platform short of the greatest practicable would not be a wise policy in view of the rapid developments in aviation...

'The British have airplane carriers ranging in displacement from 10,000 to 26,000 tons, and in speeds from 20 to 32 knots, none of which are wholly satisfactory. It is desired to give to our Naval Air Service the highest type of carrier possible with which to experiment in the construction and operation of heavier-than-air aircraft. Therefore, we should not be content to accept any speed, landing area or steadiness of platform short of the greatest practicable.'[10]

The General Board produced an additional reason for favouring the bigger of the two designs. The board felt that should this idea not work out, should aircraft-carriers prove to be ineffective, then the bigger design would produce a hull that could more easily be converted to some other use. The Secretary of the Navy endorsed the General Board's February 1921 characteristics, directing BuCon to develop them into a sketch design. The process of transforming the relatively vague set of characteristics into a preliminary design further refined the specifications. (It must be remembered that every feature in a proposed design had a cost in terms of weight, space or both. Actually trying to find room inside a proposed hull form for each of the features listed in the characteristics often revealed that the early estimates of size and weight had been over-optimistic.) Not surprisingly, the design as delivered by BuCon had grown again:

1922 Programme Aircraft-carrier:
Schemes A & B (5 May 1921)[11]

Displacement:	39,000 tons (normal)
Length:	850ft
Beam:	94ft
Draught:	29ft 8in (normal)
Speed:	34kt at 180,000shp
Range (nm/kt):	10,000/10
Armament:	16 x 6in, 12 x 5in,
	2 twin torpedo tubes
Aircraft:	n/a

BuCon was unable to resolve the characteristics into a single sketch design. Too many questions about aircraft-carrier operations remained unanswered to allow a definitive solution. Rather than make arbitrary judgments, BuCon submitted a pair of design sketches which embodied as many of the varied optional features as possible. The bureau explained the options as follows:

'The above sketches show two designs, each of which meets in general the characteristics laid down for this type of ship. The principal differences between the two are to be found in the methods of disposing of the boiler gases.

'Type A (Flush-deck type) provides a flying deck clear of permanent obstructions throughout its entire length. Type B (Island type) provides a flying deck clear of permanent obstructions except for the smoke stack, cage mast, conning tower, etc., which are located in a group at one side of the vessel, just forward of amidships. Originally a flying deck clear of obstructions was considered basic. However, with the present size of ship and length of deck, this conception is not as sound as formerly – besides, it seems necessary to be able to fly on and off at the same time – in other words, on such a long ship, there is a flying-off end and a flying-on end which may be used quite independently of

each other with a neutral zone between. The smoke stack, cranes, mast and bridge are located in this neutral zone.

'The required speed of not less than 34 knots, together with the other characteristics, force the use of the largest machinery installation so far undertaken, viz., 180,000shp – the same as that for the battlecruisers. The minimum hull has been built around this machinery with good torpedo protection, $2^3/4$-in deck and 7in side armor protection...

'In securing the entirely unobstructed flying deck, the following disadvantages or difficulties – all of which have been successfully met in type B (Island type) – have been recognized and are in a greater or lesser degree unsolved at the present time:

(a) The necessity of delivering the boiler gases from the side of the ship in such a direction and with such velocity as to preclude the possibility of their drifting back...Model experiments indicate that the gases draw in against the ship's side and cross the deck with a slight cross wind.

(b) The necessity of taking air for boiler blowers from openings in the sides forward of the stack openings and leading same aft through large distribution ducts to the boiler room intakes...

(c) The necessity of providing telescopic masts, stacks and cranes, housing radio, searchlights, signalling arrangements, pilot house and fire control station...

'In addition to providing much more satisfactory methods of meeting the problems noted in the preceding paragraph, the following additional and distinct advantages may be claimed for type B:

(d) About 8 per cent additional hangar space.

(e) Improved location and size of elevators.

(f) Increased range of radio due to permanent type of mast.

(g) Considerably more crew space available because of the smaller space inside the hull used for uptakes and air intakes...

'In view of the foregoing, specific decision is requested on the following...

(h) "Flush" deck type versus the "Island" type. The Bureau favours the "Island" type as offering a much better solution – everything considered.'[12]

As intended, the two preliminary designs set off considerable debate among the bureaux about various features of the proposed aircraft-carriers. BuOrd responded immediately with an alternative arrangement of the armament.[13] In particular, the inset turrets forward were considered to be unsatisfactory. At that location, the forward 6in guns could not be elevated past 8°, limiting them to a range of 12,000 yards and the after pair of those guns could be trained forward to only within 30° of the bow. In addition, any guns mounted so low on the bow were bound to be wet, making them unusable in weather or at speed. In their place, BuOrd suggested a pair of superimposed twin turrets forward of the island (of Scheme B) on the flight deck. (Actually, the original sketch showed a pair of turrets on the port side of the flight deck forward as well, but these were deleted from the sketch before it was submitted.) BuOrd accepted a reduction, on paper, of four guns because in reality this arrangement gave the same firepower (assuming that the forward turrets could be fired across the flight deck to port). They also objected to the arrangement of all twelve 5in guns aft in both of BuCon's sketches. Instead, they suggested that six of the guns be brought forward to an amidships position. Perhaps most important, BuOrd came out strongly in favour of the second of BuCon's sketches:

> 'The "Island" type ship (scheme B) is preferred from an ordnance point of view, as regards battery and fire control, as it furnishes the only satisfactory place for rangefinders and control stations.[14]

In an effort to satisfy BuOrd's wishes, BuCon rearranged the armament but was able to fit far fewer guns than BuOrd had proposed. The six 6in guns in BuCon's new sketch were mounted in three twin turrets, two aft and one forward in front of the island. The number of 5in AA guns remained the same but was rearranged with only eight guns aft and the other four moved to a position between the island and the forward 6in turret on the starboard side of the flight deck. The armour was also rearranged to give better protection against plunging fire. In place of a deep belt of vertical armour, 12ft 6in in depth and tapering from 7in to 4in thickness, the new sketch showed a much shallower belt topped with a sloping armoured deck 4¼-in thick (on top on ¾-in of STS), meeting the flat protective deck at the outer edge of the mechanical spaces.

The Washington Treaty

At this stage global politics intervened with a profound influence on the development of the 1922 Programme aircraft-carriers. The Washington Conference on Naval Disarmament had convened in late 1920. At first, few in the Navy thought that much would come of the affair, but it soon became clear that the five powers were intent on hammering out a real treaty. Most of the argument was about capital ships and most of that was aimed at working out how to halt the current and planned build-up. The result was an agreement on a ten-year 'holiday' in capital ship construction. All battleships and battlecruisers not already completed would be scrapped and all planned ships would be cancelled. Old warships were to be scrapped until a total displacement ratio of 5:5:3 for Great Britain, the USA and Japan was achieved.[15] No capital ship could be replaced until it was at least 20 years old and then it could be no larger than 35,000 tons. The USA and Britain agreed to a limit of approximately 500,000 tons; the other nations would be allowed proportionately less. Agreement on these points was arrived at surprisingly easily.

The same proportions were to apply to aircraft-carriers, although there was considerably less certainty as to how to handle this category. After all, at that time only Great Britain had any practical experience with the type. The original proposal was for 80,000 tons each for the USA and Britain, but there was general agreement that this was too small; the final terms were 135,000 tons each for the two major powers with each individual hull limited to 27,000 tons. The USA agreed on the condition that it be allowed to convert two of the battlecruiser hulls now scheduled for scrapping. These were to be allowed a one-time exemption from the individual hull tonnage limitation; they were to be limited to 33,000 tons each.[16]

The idea of converting one or more battlecruiser hulls into an aircraft-carrier had been percolating ever since it had been formally proposed in 1920, during the hearings over the 1921 Navy Bill.[17] Once raised, the idea was kept alive in Congress, although it had little support from the Navy. But as the design of the 1922 Programme aircraft-carrier evolved and grew, it had become essentially as large as the battlecruisers hulls that now, due to the Washington Treaty, were being offered for conversion. The treaty was not officially signed until 1 February 1922, but on 20 January the CNO recommended to the Navy Secretary that the General Board be requested to take a fresh look at the characteristics of the proposed aircraft-carriers. The Secretary of the Navy concurred four days later.[18]

Battlecruisers into Aircraft-Carriers

The design process to date had resulted in plans for a ship so close to a battlecruiser in size and general shape that the changes necessary to build the 1922 Programme aircraft-carrier on the hull of a 'Lexington'-class battlecruiser were relatively minor. It took only until 17 February 1922 for the General Board to develop a revised set of characteristics:

1922 Programme Aircraft-Carrier: Battle-cruiser Conversion (18 February 1922)[19]

Displacement:	33,000-36,000 tons (standard)
Length:	850ft
Beam:	104ft 10in
Draught:	24ft 2in (standard)
Speed:	34kt at 180,000shp
Range (nm/kt):	10,000/10
Armament:	8 x 8in, 12 x 5in, 2 twin torpedo tubes
Aircraft:	72

This design married the existing battlecruiser hulls to the desired characteristics of a big, fast aircraft-carrier. Much more detail was available in the lower decks, compared with the previous sketches, since these were already built into the partially completed hulls and would not need to be changed (and would, in fact, be very expensive to change) in the conversion. The gun armament had been considerably strengthened as a direct consequence of complaints by the War Plans Division that the proposed 6in battery was too weak.[20] The forward guns were now arranged at flight deck level, the 8in guns in superfiring twin mountings immediately forward of the island and the 5in battery in groups of three on each side of the flight deck:

'In every new design conflicting requirements have to be adjusted. The installation of four 8-inch guns forward on the starboard side of the converted vessel will take up deck space which might otherwise be used for aviation purposes. Anti-aircraft guns forward on both sides also reduce the deck space available for aviation purposes. The General Board, however, after considering these questions, recommends the installation of the guns at the expense of clear deck space. Should experience in service, and the development of tactics justify the removal of the guns, they can be removed with less expense and delay than would be entailed were they omitted now from the design and later had to be installed.'[21]

Something had to give in order to add more weight in guns. Armour was sacrificed; the

Above: Looking aft along *Lexington*'s flight deck as the ship begins to take on the appearance of an aircraft-carrier, April 1926. Note the funnel uptakes on the left, not yet projecting above the deck. The aft main battery mountings, lacking guns, are in place, but the forward ones wait on the flight deck to the right. Large holes in the flight deck remain, covered with canvas and plywood, to allow major equipment to be lowered into the hangar. (NARA)

armoured belt was now to be only 9ft 4in deep and it sloped outwards, as in the battlecruiser design. The armoured deck was also reduced in thickness over most of its length.

'It would be possible to reduce machinery weights by about 2,000 tons and to assign weight thus saved to retention of more side protection, with a corresponding reduction in speed to about 27½ knots. This procedure is not recommended as the General Board regards high speed as an essential characteristic of an aircraft-carrier.'[22]

Overall, the General Board was pleased with the resulting design. The main problem with the conversion was displacement. The sketch designs had grown to 39,000 tons while the Washington Treaty limited the battlecruiser conversions to 33,000 tons. Fortunately, the treaty included a clause that allowed the addition of up to 3,000 tons added protection in the form of hull blisters (or bulges) or deck armour to existing ships. The US chose to interpret this as allowing the converted aircraft-carriers to displace 36,000 tons since they were being converted from a pre-existing design:[23]

'The Treaty relating to the Limitation of Naval Armament, Chapter I, Article IX, permits the conversion of two battlecruisers to aircraft-carriers, each of not more than 33,000 tons standard displacement. Chapter II, Part 3, Section 1(d) permits aircraft-carriers to be reconstructed for the purpose of defense against air and submarine attack, by equipping them with bulge or blister or anti-air attack deck protection, provided that the increase of displacement thus effected does not exceed 3,000 tons displacement for each ship. Since this additional defence is considered important, it is proposed to take advantage of the permission granted in the Treaty and the design is accordingly based upon a standard displacement of 33,000 tons and 3,000 tons additional for bulge or blister or anti-air attack deck protection.'[24]

The Navy Secretary concurred with this interpretation of the treaty, but the issue of the interpretation of this language would arise again.

The problem with the displacement limit imposed by the treaty, whether 33,000 tons or 36,000 tons, was that it was a firm limit, something warship designers naturally hate. After all, it is the nature of warship designs that they increase in weight as the design process progresses because additional features are always discovered that one bureau or another requires in the design. That was the case with the new aircraft-carriers as well. The difference was that there was, in this case, no option to add weight to the design. For example:

'...it now appears that the original design might be improved by the addition of certain machinery weights which would cause the originally designed displacement to be somewhat exceeded.

'These airplane carriers are converted from battlecruisers to airplane carriers. The General Board learns that the electrical power provided in the original designs for the battlecruiser did not suffice for the needs of the ship as converted to an airplane carrier. This is the reason for the increase in electrical power. Further, it has appeared desirable to provide additional weights in the shape of diesel engines as additional auxiliary electrical generators in order to increase the efficiency of the vessel.

'The General Board believes that in making estimates for these weights the Department should not depart in any way from the methods of estimates hitherto used and as were used by the United States in estimating tonnage at the Conference for the Limitation of Armaments, except the elimination of fuel and reserve feed water as expressly provided in the treaty. To do otherwise would not be carrying out an international treaty in good faith.'[25]

Altogether, these added items would have increased the planned displacement by 371 tons.[26] Of this increase, 196 tons was to have been offset by weights to be removed from the design. The rest would be accounted for by reducing the loads of some stores and fresh water, weights included in the definition of standard displacement. The General Board, however, disapproved the 100 tons earmarked for the auxiliary diesel generators; they allowed only the 75 tons for the increased main electrical plant, to be compensated by reduced loads.

Not surprisingly, BuAer did not like the increased gun armament:

'It is the opinion of the Bureau of Aeronautics that these guns not only take up very necessary deck space but that they also constitute an unnecessary menace to flying personnel in flying on and flying off the carrier...The justification of encroaching on the flying deck space is apparent in the case of the 8in guns but it is not apparent, in the opinion of the Bureau of Aeronautics, in the case of the 5in guns...

'It is further noted that the installation of the 8in turret on each side aft reduces the width of the flying-on deck to 60 feet for a distance of approximately 136 feet.'[27]

BuAer made clear again its opposition to the installation of torpedo tubes on the 'Lexingtons', insisting that torpedo planes could provide any necessary defence. This time the bureau added the argument that the space formerly devoted to the torpedo tubes could be far better used for much-needed shop facilities. BuAer's arguments had remained essentially unchanged since the beginning of the debate.

At the end of 1922, the debate over the design of the Navy's new aircraft-carriers ceased to be academic. The necessary Congressional authorization to convert two battlecruisers into aircraft-carriers, and partial funding for the work, came in the summer of 1922. The Navy predicted that the conversion would take 2½ years and cost $23 million for each ship. Of the six battlecruisers that had been ordered, the two hulls best suited for the conversion were *Lexington* (CC1) and *Saratoga* (CC3); these two were the furthest along in construction, the shell plating being complete nearly up to the main deck, but most of the interior fittings were finished only to the lower platform deck. Thus they were in nearly ideal condition to be converted. The propulsion systems, which would probably be retained intact, were in place, but such other major internal features as the barbettes for the four massive turrets had not yet been installed. Contracts for the conversion of *Lexington* and *Saratoga* were signed in October and November 1922.[28]

Finalizing the Design

The signing of the contracts did not mean that the design process was complete. BuAer continued its efforts to increase the aviation features of the 'Lexingtons', if necessary at the expense of armament or speed. At this point BuAer acquired a powerful boost to its arguments. *Langley* had been commissioned in March 1922 and immediately began supplying exactly what the bureau had hitherto been lacking: practical experience with an operating aircraft-carrier. Reinforced by this initial accumulation of data, BuAer renewed its demands on 11 July 1923, calling again for the flight deck of the new aircraft-carriers to be widened aft and the aft 8in guns, if retained, to be repositioned. There were further requests:

'From information received from aboard, and confirmed by officers of the *Langley*...it also appears necessary that the forward port side of the deck be entirely clear. Present plans show three (3) 5in AA guns and two (2) saluting in this location. The presence of those obstructions would seriously interfere with fighting planes flying off, and all types of planes flying on from the bow, involving considerable risk to personnel and planes.'[29]

BuCon responded to BuAer's complaints with a pair of options, but not before warning again that treaty displacement limits severely restricted these options. Weights added anywhere on the hull would have to be matched by equivalent reductions elsewhere:

'The increase in breadth of the flying deck would so restrict the fire of the two after 8in twin mounts if these were retained, as to make the retention of these guns unjustifiable. The arc of fire would be reduced to about 45

degrees and no fire dead aft would be possible... As a consequence, conferences on this subject have been held with representatives of the Bureaus of Ordnance and Aeronautics...This plan shows two new arrangements of main battery, both contemplating the elimination of the two after 8in enclosed mounts. In one the two present forward are retained with one twin 8in mount abaft the smoke pipe structure, and in the other a substitution for the whole 8in battery is made in two triple mounts, one forward and one aft. Either of these arrangements can be accomplished on the weight available, provided the three anti-aircraft guns on the port side forward are also omitted, as recommended by the Bureau of Aeronautics.'[30]

Despite BuCon's claim that BuOrd had been consulted before it submitted its pair of main battery proposals, that bureau did not like BuCon's choices, which positively promoted aviation features at the expense of armament. BuOrd correctly noted that both of BuCon's options would reduce both the 8in and 5in batteries by 25 per cent. The bureau claimed that the battery size of eight 8in and twelve 5in guns had been arrived at through months of deliberation and had received the blessing of the General Board, and was the minimum armament that BuOrd was prepared to accept.[31]

As always, the General Board was responsible for moderating the debate and retained the ultimate say on the characteristics of the 'Lexingtons'. On 11 October 1923, they pronounced that BuAer's requests were reasonable and had to be implemented. Specifically, they stated that the widening of the flight deck aft and the concomitant relocation of the aft 8in mountings to a site on the flight deck had to be accomplished. The additional 250 tons that these changes would weigh would have to be compensated by sacrifices elsewhere.[32]

The weight reductions were to be obtained by eliminating two of the three planned catapults (one forward and one aft to be removed – leaving one forward) for a saving of 42 tons, by removing one of the sixteen boilers (which would reduce top speed by only 1/2 knot) for a saving of 65 tons, by once again deleting the proposed auxiliary diesel-electric plant which had somehow been reinstated in the ships' plans (arguing that the main steam-generating plant could never be shut down, not even when the ships were in port, so the proposed auxiliary plant really was redundant) for a saving of 102 tons and by reducing 5in

Above: *Saratoga* was further advanced in April 1926. Her funnel, still shrouded in scaffolding, is largely complete and her main battery mountings have their weapons in place. Note the 5in mounting, minus the gun barrel, in the sponson in the foreground. (NARA)

ammunition by 50 tons for total of 259 tons of weight reduction.[33] This weight reduction would allow BuAer's proposed changes to be made without reducing the gun battery:

'Spreading the flying deck aft to a width of 84 feet and providing a ramp at the taffrail make it necessary to remove the after 8-inch guns to a place just abaft the "island" arranged in vertical echelon in two turrets. This unsymmetrical placing of the battery involves an increased list to the ship when fully loaded. If a boiler be removed from the starboard side, this list will be reduced.

'The Bureau of Aeronautics requests the removal of the port bow group of three 5-inch from its present location to some other place, either on the next deck below or well aft on the port side. The Board is informed that it will not be objectionable as a construction feature to arrange both starboard and port anti-aircraft batteries on the next deck below, somewhat similarly to the same batteries aft. While such a change is not required by the Bureau of Aeronautics for the starboard bow battery, the

fact that those three guns are in danger from the blast of the forward 8-inch guns, and the change would decrease to some extent the difficulties of flying off, the Board recommends that both batteries be dropped to the next lower deck.'[34]

BuCon took these directions and produced a set of final plans for submission to the Navy Secretary. The batteries were rearranged based on the General Board's decision and two of the three catapults were deleted. The diesel generating plant was deleted from the plans, but space was reserved and accesses provided so that a later decision to reinstate this item could be accommodated without difficulty. Since both hulls were essentially finished up to the third deck, meaning that the engineering plants were essentially complete, BuCon concluded that it would be no easier to remove the sixteenth boiler now than it would be to take it out later, when the ships' weights would be known more accurately. The only problem area

Above: Almost complete, the only work now being done on *Lexington* in April 1927 is the construction of her fore and mainmast structures with their multiple control tops. (NARA)

was in the reduction of 5in ammunition stowage. It was not sufficient under the terms of the treaty simply to delete stowage fittings for some number of 5in rounds, while leaving the magazine spaces as planned for the larger allowance. Based on the General Board's stated desire that ammunition reduction be done only as the last resort, BuCon felt it would be best to proceed with fitting the planned spaces for a full allowance of 400 rounds per gun and reduce those spaces later by whatever amount was necessary to meet treaty limits.[35]

The Navy Secretary noted and approved all BuCon's recommendations, instructing the bureau to proceed with the conversion based on the plans submitted on 21 December 1923.[36] This should have finalized the plans for the 'Lexingtons'.

The 3,000 Tons

The issue of the correct allowable displacement of the 'Lexingtons' refused to go away. It was raised again in the process of preparing the 1924 Ship's Data Book, a biennial publication that gave basic technical specifications for all US Navy ships. BuCon's problem was how to show the 'Lexingtons' displacement. The bureau

turned to the Navy Secretary for guidance, asking for a choice between three options: the 'Lexingtons' could be listed as displacing 33,000 tons (which was the basic treaty standard displacement); 36,000 tons (the actual treaty standard displacement); or 38,665 tons (which was a 36,000-ton standard displacement translated into normal displacement to make it consistent with all the other displacements in the Ship's Data Book).[37] The issue, as BuCon saw it, went far beyond this one publication: a decision had to be made as to which displacement the Navy wanted to state for the record, since that figure would be used in calculating how much tonnage remained under the treaty limits for future aircraft-carrier construction. The acting Secretary, Teddy Roosevelt, turned the matter over to the General Board, which instructed BuCon to use the lowest of the figures, with a footnote indicating that the ships really displaced 3,000 more tons as allowed under the treaty. Specifically, they directed that the two ships would be charged at 33,000 tons each for the purpose of calculating allowable tonnage for future construction.[38]

This solution was not to last; Roosevelt was replaced by a permanent Navy Secretary,

Curtis Wilbur, who opened up the issue once more. Secretary Wilbur took the position that the 3,000 tons allowed by the treaty could not legitimately be used in the case of the 'Lexingtons'. He therefore ordered the General Board on 26 May 1925 to recommend a solution. The Secretary was expecting nothing less than major surgery:

'Your attention is directed to the tonnage of the aircraft carriers *Lexington* and *Saratoga*. You are directed to immediately take up the question as to what changes in these ships should be made in order to reduce their tonnage to 33,000 tons.

'Pending your decision and action thereon, I have directed the Bureau of Construction and Repair and the Bureau of Ordnance to suspend all operations looking toward the mounting of the guns on these ships and the placing of additional armor thereon. I understand that the omission of guns and side armor on these ships would reduce their tonnage over 2,800 tons and that additional savings in reserve feed water, etc., may reduce the tonnage below 33,000 tons.'[39]

The Board's response was that any solution would involve a serious reduction in one or more major military capabilities:

'There are three attributes of these ships that may be modified to reduce their displacement by 3,000 tons, namely, their speed, their battery and their armor. The reduction cannot be accomplished under any circumstances without reducing the speed — neither the sacrifice of all of the armour nor all of the battery, or even both of these combined, will provide the required reduction in weight.

'Being thus forced to reduce the machinery weights, we find that a reduction of one-quarter of the power will leave these ships with a speed of 32.25 knots. By the sacrifice of one-half of the horsepower we will be able to retain a speed of 29.25 knots. No other fractional reduction is feasible without redesigning practically the entire machinery plant.'[40]

There were three specific options included in the General Board's reply. Option A reduced both armour and power by half. This option would have kept the battery intact but left the ships with armour only on the scale of a contemporary treaty cruiser.[41] Option B would have reduced power by a quarter, removed all the side armour and reduced the 8in battery by a quarter and the 5in battery by a third. This option would have left the ships practically defenceless in any close engagement. Option C

called for a 50 per cent reduction in power and reductions in armament similar to Option B. The General Board came down strongly in favour of the third option as the least harmful of the three:[42]

While the General Board was willing to go along with Secretary Wilbur's request for options to reduce the 'Lexingtons' tonnage, it still wanted to convince the Secretary that the whole idea of reducing the tonnage by that amount was dangerous and, more importantly, unnecessary. To help them make their case, they recruited the help of Assistant Navy Secretary Robinson. On 30 June 1925 Robinson wrote to Wilbur while the latter was travelling in California, stating that the General Board now believed that the correct interpretation of the treaty's language allowed that tonnage actually used for added deck protection and for the blister. This tonnage came to 1,805 tons and could legitimately be added to the basic 33,000 tons. Therefore, it was only necessary to lose 1,195 tons and this could be done by reducing power by one-quarter and some minor savings in structural weights.[43]

The matter had been taken up with the Secretary of State and received the approval of that department. Robinson was taking no chances. Secretary Wilbur's scribbled approval of this approach can be seen at the bottom of the letter. Despite Wilbur's scribble, no action was taken on the issue during the next few months, prompting the General Board to express its frustration in a surprisingly candid letter dated 23 August 1925.[44] It reiterated that it had studied the issue from all sides and had placed a well reasoned recommendation on the Secretary's desk, but nothing seemed to be happening. Now a new issue had arisen. The focus had shifted from legality to practicality. The real problem that the Secretary had to address was how to get the ships built:

'The estimates of the Bureau of Construction and Repair and the Bureau of Engineering show that two new factors have entered to complicate the situation, one is time, the other is money. So far as national defense is concerned, time is the more important. The conversion of these ships to aircraft carriers was authorized July 1, 1922, still they are not in the water operating with the fleet.'[45]

The pressure to stop the debate and get the job done was building. The original $23 million price tag had grown to $40 million each and the schedule had slipped from 30 to 67 months.[46] With these factors now firmly in focus, BuCon

Left: Putting the finishing touches to *Lexington's* foremast, April 1927. The completed chart-house and pilot-house are located between the aft legs of the tripod at navigation bridge level. The main battery fire control top and the 5in control top are still under construction. (NARA)

and BuEng had submitted proposals that would reduce the tonnage more quickly or more inexpensively than ripping out a quarter of the powerplant. BuOrd's suggestion was to remove the 'Lexingtons'' armoured belt.[47] The General Board came out in favour of this approach.[48]

The Navy Secretary continued to procrastinate. CinCUS joined the debate with his recollections of the treaty negotiations. He recalled that, at the time, the Royal Navy had already added the extra protection to most of its ships and fully intended to continue until all its

ships had the extra protection. This included the still unfinished battlecruiser HMS *Renown*. The US agreed to go along as long as the US Navy also had the right to add extra protection, under the infamous Section 1(d), to all its ships, including the 'Lexingtons'.[49] This argument seems to have convinced Secretary Wilbur, but still no decision was forthcoming. Finally, on 4 March 1926, BuCon had run out of patience:

'...instructions in regard to the removal of side armor were prepared but were not actually issued to the contractors, as it appeared on conference with the Secretary of the Navy that it would be advisable to defer the removal of the armor until such time as the progress of the work required definite action to be taken. No work either of installation or of removal of side armor has since been done.

'The Bureau understands informally that, as a result of additional information bearing on the subject, the Department has decided that a reduction of the final displacement of these vessels...is not required, and that the vessels may be completed in accordance with the plans previously approved...

'As the construction of the vessels has now arrived at the point where it will shortly be necessary to issue final instructions relative to the side armor, if delay in completion is to be avoided, confirmation or correction of the above understanding is requested.'[50]

Finally, the next day, Secretary Wilbur, in a one-sentence letter, laid the matter to rest:

'The understanding of the Bureau...is correct, and the Bureau will be governed accordingly.'[51]

On 8 March 1926 BuCon issued instructions to the two shipyards to complete the work on the 'Lexingtons' as planned.

Into the Fleet
Construction of the two aircraft-carriers now progressed rapidly. *Lexington* was commissioned on 14 December 1927 at Quincy, MA; *Saratoga* had been commissioned a month earlier, on 16 November 1927, at Camden, NJ.[52] After brief post-commissioning yard visits, the 'Lexingtons' sailed for the West Coast, stopping only long enough to pick up their air groups at Hampton Roads. Once through the Panama Canal, they came under the command of CinC Battle Fleet.[53] After a period of trials, the two new aircraft-carriers joined the Battle Fleet, as the US Navy's Pacific Fleet was then known.

During the period between the World Wars, the US Navy held annual Fleet Problems to test some aspect of the fleet's strategy and tactics in preparation for the next war, a war that many in the US Navy saw inevitably approaching in the Pacific. The first such exercise in which the 'Lexingtons' participated was Fleet Problem IX held in January 1929. The fleet was split into two groups: Blue forces protecting the Panama Canal and Black forces attacking. *Lexington* was assigned to the Blue forces, primarily conducting scouting activities. *Saratoga* was assigned to the Black fleet and was made the

nucleus of a Striking Force. The plan was innovative:

'23 January
0000 – *Saratoga* and *Omaha* proceeding without further escort on wide detour to the Southward in order to approach Panama Gulf from the South; join with battleships of striking force on the morning of the 26th at a designated position in the Gulf of Panama, then launch bombing attack on the canal. Battleships of striking force (four long-range BBs) proceeding with destroyer escort (18 DDs) at reduced speed on more Easterly course to this designated rendezvous with the *Saratoga* on the morning (0600) of the 26th. This separation of striking force units, contrary to the original plan, was occasioned by a shortage of fuel in the destroyers and a desire to adhere to that part of the original plan which contemplated a similar detour by the entire striking force permitting an approach from the South instead of from the West.'[54]

The approach from the south was not without incident. *Saratoga* was theoretically sunk by a defending cruiser at 1922 on the 25th, but the exercise continued and *Saratoga* launched a strike of 83 aircraft at 0458 on the 26th that, again in theory, completely destroyed the canal. All the players understood the artificiality of the scenario and the weakness of the attack plan.[55] All understood as well that a new and powerful factor had entered into the equations of naval strategy and tactics.

1. GenBd, CNO -> GenBd, 7 June 1920, Air Craft Carriers. The quote is from an attached memorandum from Captain Craven to the CNO, dated 6 May 1920.
2. Fox, p41.
3. There can be no doubt that this is exactly what Mitchell had in mind. He was trying to reproduce in the US what had happened in England, where the Royal Air Force had been formed with command of all aircraft, land- or carrier-based. The Royal Navy's experience between the wars and in the Second World War proved how disastrous this arrangement was.
4. BuCon, Memorandum, 29 January 1921.
5. GenBd, CNO -> GenBd, 7 June 1920, Air Craft Carriers. The quote is from an attached memorandum from Captain Craven to the CNO, dated 6 May 1920. This is the same memo quoted in Note 1.
6. BuCon, BuCon -> SecNav, 12 November 1920, Scout Cruisers altered for use as Aircraft carriers (4th Endorsement).
7. GenBd, GenBd -> SecNav, 16 December 1920, Scout Cruisers altered for use as Aircraft carriers.
8. GenBd, Memorandum, 6 November 1920, Air Plane Carriers.
9. GenBd, GenBd -> SecNav, 24 February 1921, Building Programme, 1922: Characteristics for Airplane Carriers.
10. ibid. This quote is from an attachment entitled Memorandum to Accompany Characteristics for Airplane Carriers. This memo could have been written

by BuAer; it so closely resembles in all its logic the line of argument adopted by the naval aviation community during the design and building of the 'Lexingtons'.

11. SecNav, BuCon -> SecNav, 12 May 1921, Building Programme, 1922: Characteristics for Airplane Carriers. These specifications are derived from this memo and from the accompanying sketch designs dated 5 May 1921.

12. ibid.

13. SecNav, BuOrd -> SecNav, 20 May 1921, Building Programme, 1922: Characteristics for Airplane Carriers.

14. ibid. Note that while no correspondence from BuAer dating from this period was found in the GenBd or SecNav files, there can be little doubt that they favoured Scheme A. At this early stage of aircraft-carrier development, BuAer consistently favoured a flush deck arrangement.

15. France and Italy signed, accepting half the tonnage allowed Japan.

16. Baker, Arthur, *Battlefleets and Diplomacy: Naval Disarmament Between the Two World Wars*, WI, No 3, 1989, pp224-226.

17. Fox, p64. Senator William H. King raised the issue. Captain Craven, who was present at the hearings, was lukewarm at best.

18. GenBd, CNO -> SecNav, 20 January 1922, Airplane Carriers – conversion of battle cruisers into. The Navy Secretary's endorsement to this is dated 24 January 1922.

19. These specifications were taken directly from a document entitled Converted Airplane Carriers, 1922: Characteristics which was originally attached to a GenBd letter dated 17 February 1922, cited below, and from a sketch design dated 18 February 1922.

20. SecNav, DirWarPlans -> CNO, 25 November 1921, Building Programme 1922: Characteristics for Airplane Carriers.

21. SecNav, GenBd Memorandum, 17 February 1922, Converted Airplane Carriers, 1922: Characteristics. The memorandum was an enclosure to a GenBd letter of the same date. The quote is Note 1 from that enclosure.

22. ibid. Note 2.

23. The exact language included in the treaty clause in question (Chap 2, Pt 3, Sect 1(d)) reads (in part): 'Reconstruction of capital ships and aircraft carriers shall be limited to providing new means of defense against air and submarine attack. The Contracting Powers may, for that purpose, equip existing tonnage with bulge or blister, or anti-air attack deck protection, provided the increase of displacement thus affected does not exceed 3,000 standard tons (3,048 metric tons).' Despite the fact that the 'Lexingtons'' design made use of all 36,000 tons allowed by the treaty, official Navy documents consistently listed their tonnage as 33,000 tons, with the extra tonnage shown in a footnote.

24. GenBd, BuCon -> SecNav, 22 April 1922, Building Programme 1922 – Battle Cruisers 1 – 6 Class, converted to Airplane Carriers.

25. GenBd, GenBd -> SecNav, 18 September 1922, Airplane Carriers – Battle Cruisers Converted – Estimated weights for (1st Endorsement). Part of the confusion over how to estimate the displacement of the new aircraft-carriers was the fact that tonnage was to be calculated under the treaty in a different manner from that which the Americans were used to. The US Navy traditionally used 'normal' tonnage for its ships, which is defined as: '...vessel fully equipped and ready for sea with two-thirds full supply of stores and fuel and with full supply of ammunition.' The Washington treaty, however, used tonnage based on 'standard' displacement, which was defined as: '...displacement of the ship complete, fully

manned, engined, and equipped ready for sea, including all armament and ammunition, equipment, outfit, provisions and fresh water for crew, miscellaneous stores and implements of every description that are intended to be carried in war, but without fuel or reserve feed water on board.' Obviously, this gave a different displacement, calculated in a manner with which the US Navy was not familiar. (Both quotes are from the cited letter.)

26. GenBd, SecNav -> BuCon, 22 August 1922, Airplane Carriers – Battle Cruisers Converted – Estimated weights for (3rd Endorsement).

27. SecNav, BuAer -> BuCon, 23 March 1922, Building Programme 1922 – Characteristics for Converted Airplane Carriers (5th Endorsement).

28. *Lexington* was being built at Bethlehem Steel's Fore River Yard, Quincy, MA; *Saratoga* was under construction at the New York Shipbuilding Yard, Camden, NJ. Both were completed at the same yards.

29. GenBd, BuAer -> SecNav, 11 July 1923, U.S.S. *Lexington* and *Saratoga* – Flying Deck.

30. GenBd, BuCon -> SecNav, 28 July 1923, *Lexington* and *Saratoga* (CV2) and (CV3) - Flying Deck.

31. GenBd, BuOrd -> SecNav, 6 August 1923, *Lexington* and *Saratoga* (CV2) and (CV3) - flying deck.

32. GenBd, GenBd -> SecNav, 11 October 1923, *Lexington* and *Saratoga* - Rearrangement of Battery and Flying Deck.

33. ibid.

34. ibid.

35. GenBd, BuCon -> SecNav, 21 December 1923, Aircraft carriers *Lexington* (CV2) - and *Saratoga* (CV3) - Changes in flying deck and rearrangement of battery.

36. GenBd, SecNav -> BuCon, 4 February 1924, Aircraft carriers *Lexington* (CV2) and *Saratoga* (CV3) - Changes in flying deck and rearrangement of battery. The fact that it took sixteen months after the contracts were signed to finalize the plans for the 'Lexingtons' conversion was one of the contributing factors to the delays and cost overruns that plagued their construction.

37. GenBd, BuCon -> SecNav, 30 August 1924. BuCon noted that the first two figures quoted were estimates that included a small margin for error since they followed treaty limits which could not be exceeded. The third figure contained no such margin, but added in two-thirds of the maximum load of fuel and reserve feed water to make it conform to the earlier USN practice of calculating normal displacement.

38. GenBd, GenBd -> SecNav, 11 September 1924, Displacement of airplane carriers *Lexington* and *Saratoga* (2nd Endorsement).

39. GenBd, SecNav -> GenBd, 26 May 1925.

40. SecNav, GenBd -> SecNav, 5 June 1925, Reduction of Displacement, *Lexington* and *Saratoga*.

41. The Washington Treaty regulated the number and size of cruisers that could be built. Heavy cruisers were limited to 10,000 tons displacement and an 8in main battery. To carry a main battery that large on that small a displacement, armour had to be limited to a narrow belt of 3in or 4in over a limited length. When freed from these treaty restrictions, US heavy cruisers quickly grew to 14,000 and later 17,000 tons standard displacement.

42. ibid.

43. SecNav, AsstSecNav -> SecNav, 30 June 1925.

44. SecNav, GenBd -> SecNav, 23 August 1925, Reduction in displacement of the *Lexington* and *Saratoga* (8th Endorsement).

45. ibid.

46. Fox, p94.

47. SecNav, BuOrd -> CNO, 26 September 1925, Storage of

Main Belt Armour removed from Aircraft Carriers. BuOrd had made arrangements to store *Saratoga*'s armour at NY Philadelphia and *Lexington*'s at NY Boston.

48. SecNav, GenBd -> SecNav, 23 August 1925, Reduction in displacement of the *Lexington* and *Saratoga* (8th Endorsement).

49. SecNav, CinCUS -> SecNav, undated. This letter was

marked as logged into SecNav's Secret & Confidential files on 29 October 1925.

50. SecNav, BuCon -> SecNav, 4 March 1926, Reduction in displacement of the *Lexington* and *Saratoga*.

51. SecNav, SecNav -> BuCon, 5 March 1926, Reduction in displacement of the *Lexington* and *Saratoga* (1st Endorsement).

52. The names of the new aircraft-carriers, *Lexington* and *Saratoga*, were the names given to the battlecruiser hulls on which they were built. The 'Lexington'-class battlecruisers were to have been named after famous battles in American history (e.g., *Lexington* and *Saratoga*) or famous US naval vessels (e.g., the scrapped battlecruisers *Constellation*, *Ranger*, *Constitution* and *United States*). As no further battlecruisers were planned, this naming convention was adopted for the Navy's aircraft-carriers.

53. BuCon, CNO -> Lex, 7 January 1928, USS *Lexington* – Proposed Assignment and Operations of. These ordered that the 'Lexingtons' would be home-ported at San Pedro, CA, with NY Bremerton (later known as NYPS) as their home yard.

54. FltProb, Fleet Problem IX App. V, 4 February 1929, Summary of Procedure Black Striking Force, Problem IX.

55. ibid. It will be noted that observer *Saratoga* states as his opinion that the operations of the *Saratoga* were entirely impractical as the ship was too close to the enemy air base and was inadequately protected by surface craft. Furthermore, no aircraft were detailed specifically to protect the *Saratoga* although it appears planes were on board that ship which might have been used for this purpose. Fleet Observer Black concurs to a certain degree in the above, but considers it very fortunate indeed that these deficiencies should have developed in this problem wherein large plane carriers were used for the first time, in order that these may be studied and discussed at length with a view to the taking of measures to prevent repetition.

2. Physical Characteristics

This chapter presents a physical description of the 'Lexingtons', describing what they looked like and how they worked. The first part provides a cross-section of the ships in mid-career, when the two vessels were still nearly identical, and describes the various parts of the ships physically and as locations of crew activities. It also describes the process by which the ships were modernized in peace and war. The second part describes the 'Lexingtons'' turbo-electrical propulsion system. The remaining parts describe the ships' crews, the systems for feeding and supplying the ships and the ships' sanitation systems.

2.1 Hull

From their double bottoms to their flight decks, the 'Lexingtons' were divided horizontally by nine decks. From the keel up, these decks were the hold, second and first platform decks, third deck, second or hangar deck, middle and upper half decks, main deck and flight deck. The vertical separation between decks was approximately 9ft, although this figure varied considerably throughout the ships. The sheer of the decks betrayed the ships' battlecruiser origin. The lower decks, through the third deck, were strictly horizontal, following the waterline. The next two decks, the second and middle half decks, had pronounced sheer forward, following the planned sheer line of the battlecruisers' bow. This sheer forward was incompatible with the requirement to superimpose a flat flight deck on top of the battlecruiser hull; the upper half deck and all remaining decks therefore reverted to horizontal orientation.

The ships were divided vertically by hull frames numbered 0 to 212 from the forefoot to the sternpost. While there was some variation in frame spacing, it was usually 4ft between frames. At the bow, the framing continued forward into the bow overhang; these frames were denoted by the letters A to H in ascending order from the forefoot to the foremost tip of the flight deck.

The locations of the various crew activities are given in the following paragraphs, but a few statements will help in understanding why the ships were laid out as they were. The ships could generally be divided horizontally into two main sections and vertically into three sections. The horizontal division was at the third deck. The spaces below were the area in which the crew worked to keep the ship moving through the water, lit and heated and supplied with the material necessary to fight the ship. A major warship is often likened to a floating city: in that case, this was the 'industrial district', where the city's powerplant and warehouses were located. Above the third deck, the crew slept, ate and, above all, prepared and employed their weapons, particularly the aircraft. This was the 'airport', and the apartment blocks and light industries that surrounded it. The vertical divisions split the ships into three sections, roughly bow, centre and stern. The relatively narrow bow and stern sections were used for storerooms, workshops and accommodation for the crew. The fatter centre section was given over to those major ships' functions that required the space. Below the third deck was the propulsion plant; above the third deck were hangar spaces, where the 'Lexingtons'' air groups were serviced and repaired.

Lower Decks

The lowest decks were allocated primarily to tanks for liquids, storerooms, magazines and spaces for the ships' power systems. The extreme outer shell of the ships, from the double bottom around the curve of the keel and up the sides of the hull to the level of the third deck, was made up of layers of tanks for the various liquids required to run the ships.

The huge machinery spaces began at Frame 75 and continued aft to Frame 133, being split in half by a transverse watertight bulkhead at Frame 104. Each of these compartments extended vertically from the hold through two intervening decks, its overhead formed by the third deck. Each half space was further subdivided into eleven compartments. The central part was split laterally into a pair of engine rooms and a pump room. This central area was flanked on each side by eight boiler rooms. The main control room was located immediately aft of the machinery spaces at hold level; from this compartment the entire propulsion and power system was controlled. Here could be found the banks of buss bars and

compartments were situated on the first platform deck, protected as they were by the armoured deck above, belt armour on the sides and two decks of watertight compartments below. These included the IC room, the forward and aft motor generator and distribution rooms and the central station. Each of these was critical to the ships' operations. The IC room held the ships' main telephone switchboard. The motor generator and distribution rooms provided emergency electrical power in case the main powerplant was shut down or disabled. These generators had been sacrificed in the original conversion to save weight, but were found to be essential and were reinstated to provide emergency lighting. Central station was the ships' primary damage control command centre and was also the site of the master gyrocompass. All the equipment necessary to con the ship in an emergency was located there.

Upper Decks

The third deck was the horizontal armoured deck, extending for most of the ships' length and capping the vulnerable lower decks. It was the first of the decks above the designed waterline and marked a logical dividing line between the ship activities centred below this deck and aviation activities located above. Also, all crew berthing was above the third deck. The central part of the upper decks, between the second and main decks, was taken up with the hangar, where the ships' aircraft were serviced and spare airframes were stored. The forward section of these decks was devoted largely to living quarters and storerooms. The aft section

Above: Large sections of the upper decks aft of the hangar were occupied by workshops, both for the construction and repair of ship's equipment and for aircraft maintenance. This metal shop in *Saratoga*, seen on 16 November 1944, is fairly typical of the 'Lexingtons'' interior compartments, with linoleum flooring and pipes running through and just below the overhead spaces formed by the transverse beams. (NARA)

Right: *Saratoga*'s dental clinic was busy, as might be expected since it served a population of over 2,000 men in February 1944. As with the other medical facilities, this compartment was at the bow on the second deck. The far bulkhead is the outer shell plating of the ship, its outward slope caused by the bow overhang. (NARA)

shunts which allowed the engineering staff to apply electrical power in a myriad of different combinations. This was the duty station of the engineering officer and his staff. The four motor rooms containing the eight drive motors, two on each shaft, were located immediately aft of main control. Like the central machinery spaces, these compartments stretched vertically up to the third deck. The two outboard motor rooms were well forward of the inner two. Immediately aft of each motor room was a thrust block room which held the main bearings that carried the propeller shafts through the hull plating.

Some of the ships' most important

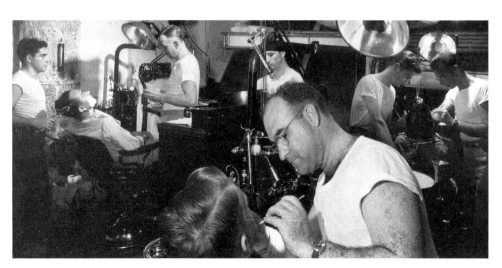

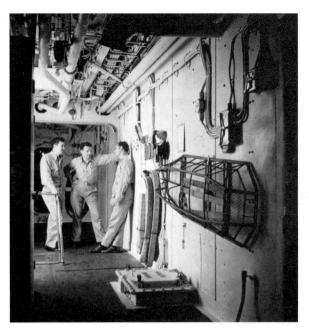

was given over to workshops and more storerooms.

The four pairs of horizontal exhaust uptakes were located amidships on the third deck. These carried the smoke from the eight port side boilers to the starboard, where it could be carried up to the funnel. The four sets of uptakes were well separated, leaving large spaces in between. The narrow air spaces around each of the individual uptakes were naturally hot and so were used as drying areas by the ships' laundry.

The second deck was also known as the hangar deck, because it formed the floor of the massive open aircraft hangar. The extreme bow of the second deck housed the ships' medical departments. The compartments in this complex included the sick bay, isolation ward, doctor's and dentist's offices, dispensary and the operating room. Here, on the starboard side, could be found the quarter deck. This was the compartment on the ships where visitors were officially received on board. The primary accommodation ladder led from the waterline to an opening in the shell plating on the port side adjacent to this compartment.

The hangar deck level was some 4ft higher than that of the second deck to accommodate the boiler uptakes that ran crossdeck at third deck level. The forward bulkhead of the hangar was at Frame 67. The forward elevator, when it was in the lowered position, formed the deck flooring of the hangar between the forward bulkhead and Frame 75. The hangar ran aft, an

unobstructed open space, nearly as wide as the ships' beam, as far as Frame 173. The small aft elevator ran between the hangar and the flight deck between Frames 114 and 122. The next two decks were called half decks because they extended only fore and aft of the hangar area. Forward on the lower of the two, the middle half deck, could be found ships' offices of various kinds, including offices for the Captain, Executive Officer, the First Lieutenant, damage control and the ordnance and supply departments.

Superstructure and External Features

The superstructure and external features of the 'Lexingtons' were far easier to change, and were therefore far more likely to be changed, than the ships' internal fixtures. Thus, it was in the external features that the two 'Lexingtons' differed the most. In general, *Lexington* was changed earlier and more often than was her sister. At their launch the two ships had been virtually identical, so much so that a large vertical black funnel stripe was painted on *Saratoga* and a horizontal one on *Lexington* to help pilots tell them apart from the air. Externally, the hulls were remarkably featureless, rising smoothly from the waterline to the flight deck. The only features that stood out were the boat pockets. These were deep insets into the hull sides at upper half deck level, extending upwards almost to the flight deck. There were five such pockets, four on the port side and one starboard. Forward of the single

Above left: A passageway at flight deck level of the island, March 1944. The fire hose and litter hanging on the bulkhead are in readiness for an emergency. This was aviator's country, most of this level of the island being occupied by a ready room, and the three young officers 'shooting the breeze' in the background are probably fliers. (NARA)

Above: *Saratoga*'s pilothouse, at navigation bridge level, contained the controls for steering and conning the ship and a chart table at which the navigator could plot the ship's course, February 1944. The helmsman in the foreground is looking into a pair of compass repeaters; his left hand is on a swinging lever used to steer the ship in place of the traditional wheel. (NARA)

Above: The chart-house was located directly aft of the pilot-house on the navigation bridge level. *Saratoga*'s navigator (right) works on a chart while the lieutenant jg in the foreground flips through the recent dispatches, leaning on a situation board used to track all known forces, friendly or enemy, November 1943. (NARA)

bulkhead of this gun position ran straight aft to a point, near Frame 201, where the tapering line of the hull intersected the straight edge of the flight deck. (In the late 1930s *Lexington* had a further gun platform at each bow and quarter. Each of these had room for three .50cal machine-guns, later modified by the replacement of one of the .50s on each sponson by a single 3in AA gun. *Saratoga* was not fitted with the new sponsons at that time. The evolution of the 'Lexingtons' gun armament is covered in detail in Chapter 4.)

At the time of their launch the 'Lexingtons' carried a total of seven anchors: three big, stockless main anchors at the bow, one each on the centreline and to port and starboard, and four smaller kedge anchors at the stern, each weighing 6,000lb, to help prevent the ships from swinging at anchor. These were housed in vertical hawse pipes, two on each side, under the overhang of the flight deck right aft. These small anchors were deleted during early refits as a weight-saving measure.[1]

The flight deck was a basically rectangular platform, narrowed aft to make room for the AA battery and tapering towards the bow. The steel understructure was covered by thick planks of wood to provide better traction for aircraft wheels in wet weather. Along most of the edge of the flight deck, there were rope life nets designed to catch deckhands who accidentally, or on purpose, went over the side of the ship. (When an aircraft went out of control on deck, sometimes the only safe place for the deck crew was over the side.) The netting extended from the bow to the aft end of the flight deck, interrupted above the AA sponsons to give

starboard boat pocket, at the same level on the starboard side, were a series of openings for air ducts to provide ventilation to the lower decks. There were a total of 28 of these; the forward six were somewhat smaller than the rest and were grouped apart.

The smooth line of the hull was broken at main deck level by four sponsons, one on each bow and quarter, each holding three 5in AA guns. Technically only the forward platforms were sponsons, meaning projections out from the hull; aft, the 5in gun positions were really long insets into the hull created by narrowing the flight deck aft of Frame 160. The inboard

Right: *Saratoga*'s open navigation bridge, forward of the pilot-house, had distinguished visitors on 9 December 1944. A Congressional delegation led by Representative Smith (centre) had come out to Pearl Harbor and was being shown around by CinCPac, Admiral Chester Nimitz (right) and *Saratoga*'s CO, Captain L.A. Moebus. (NARA)

those guns free arcs of fire and also alongside the island and funnel structures. (The remaining features of the flight deck, including the arrester gear and elevators, are covered in detail in Chapter 4.)

The massive island and funnel structures dominated the starboard side of the flight deck. This included four twin 8in gun mountings, two at flight deck level and the other two one level higher. Above the flight deck, the island structure had eight levels. These were the: aerological platform, comprising the meteorology and the Air Department offices; communications platform, dominated by the main radio cabin; navigation bridge, including the chart-house and pilot-house; flag bridge, including flag radio and the flag plot; searchlight platform, which was simply the open roof of the flag bridge; main radio compass station, which was suspended from the underside of the lower top; lower top, including the forward 8in gun director; and upper top, holding two side-by-side 5in directors and altimeters.

The 20ft main battery rangefinder was mounted on the pilothouse roof at the flag bridge level. This was a far from ideal location for this instrument and according to the inspectors in 1931: 'The space available on the flag bridge is not sufficient, due principally to the fact that the rangefinder forward on this level is just at the height of a man's eyes and prevents clear vision ahead.'[2] On *Saratoga* at that time the flag bridge level was more

developed, being built up similar to the navigation bridge. The main battery rangefinder was carried on the roof of the enlarged flag plot.

The massive funnel existed to carry the four boiler uptakes to a sufficient height above the flight deck. At the lower levels, compartments were built into the funnel itself and at higher levels crew stations were built onto the outer shell of the funnel structure. The aft end of the funnel structure, at flight deck level, held the main radio transmitter room. At the next level up, the forward part of the funnel was used for a pair of large fresh water tanks. Projecting forward at this level into the space between the funnel and the island on *Lexington* was a guntub for a single 3in AA gun; *Saratoga* had no 3in AA guns at that time. Twin 6pdr saluting guns were mounted on the roof of the fresh-water tanks.

The higher level structures built onto the outside of the funnel included, on the forward face, the enclosed secondary conning station surmounted by the open aviation control station (known as 'Pri-Fly'). On the aft face of the funnel were structures built around a free-standing bipod mainmast, repeating the gun control stations on the foremast. These included an 8in fire control station and, at the next higher level, a rectangular platform holding two 5in directors and altimeters. At one level below the top of the funnel, the fifth level, *Lexington* had AA platforms on both long sides of the funnel. These had 36in searchlights at each corner and six

Left: The 'Lexingtons' were built with a tripod foremast that towered over the island structure. This view shows *Lexington* in August 1929. The only full bridge level was the navigation bridge. The main battery rangefinder is on the pilot-house roof. Above that are the radio compass (DF) booth, the two-level main battery director top and the 5in control top with its separate directors and altimeters (two of each), the former behind the tall splinter shield and the latter on the wings. (NARA)

single .50cal machine-guns on each side. *Saratoga* was never fitted with these platforms, and her searchlights were mounted on the starboard side of the funnel only, on individual platforms carried at the fourth level of the funnel, accessible from a long catwalk that ran from the secondary conning station back to the aft main battery fire control station.

Modernization

The 'Lexingtons' were designed and built before the US Navy had any practical experience of operating large aircraft-carriers, and experience with the diminutive *Langley*, hardly of comparable characteristics, came too late to have much influence. It is a credit to the design process that the ships emerged in basically satisfactory shape. Nevertheless, as experience began to accumulate, the 'Lexingtons' needed to be regularly modified to apply operational innovations and to keep up with the rapid evolution of aircraft and other weapons.

The Modernization Process

The modernization of US Navy warships followed two distinct tracks: gradual modification, aimed at resolving relatively minor problems that had been revealed in day-to-day operations; and major reconstruction, aimed at dealing with an accumulation of serious deficiencies that were impossible to rectify within the gradual modification process. These

two processes differed in almost all aspects: in who instigated the process, in how the changes were planned and approved and in how much time it took to accomplish the desired changes. In an ideal world, these were two completely distinct processes, but economic, political and military realities led to a blurring of the distinction between the two in the case of the 'Lexingtons', particularly as war drew closer.

The ShipAlt Process

The process of gradual change involved the generation of requests for ship alterations or repairs. These could be generated by anyone in the chain of command from the ships' COs up to the fleet or type commander. Before the war a ship alteration request (ShipAlt) required endorsements up the line through the CNO, and even then were often left unfulfilled because the money might not be available. (All ShipAlts were funded from money appropriated by Congress to the Navy to cover all regular repairs and minor alterations. There were always more demands on this money than could be met.) If the work was finally funded, it was generally scheduled to be done during the ship's next yard period. Between the wars the 'Lexingtons' were scheduled for regular yard periods approximately every 18 to 24 months. These would last about three months and include drydocking to clean and repaint the ship's bottom. In addition, there would generally be a shorter yard period about

Right: A short bipod mainmast supported similar structures at the aft end of the funnel, *Lexington*, 23 January 1928. The flag of the Secretary of the Navy flies from the foremast. (NARA)

midway through this cycle to perform urgent maintenance and alterations.

Once war had broken out, the whole ShipAlt process was streamlined. It became faster and easier for a ship to get problems fixed. Money ceased to be the chief restraint. Now the ruling considerations were weight (BuShips was perennially concerned with top weight, particularly on older ships like the 'Lexingtons'), material availability (was the requested equipment available at the yard the same time that the ship was there) and military necessity (was the alteration really necessary or could the resources be better applied elsewhere). A good example of this process can be found in a ShipAlt generated by Captain J. H. Cassady, *Saratoga*'s CO, on 10 June 1944. In Alteration Request No. 26-44, *Saratoga* asked for the relocation and extension of the catwalk that ran along the inboard face of the funnel. Each ShipAlt had a section for a justification of the request, which in this case read as follows:

> 'At present there is no ready access from the Bridge to the Secondary Control Station located at the after end of the stack. This extension will make it unnecessary to descend to the Flight Deck, proceed aft 160 feet between parked or operating aircraft, and climb a vertical ladder to the Bridge level, in order for personnel ordinarily stationed on the Bridge to man Battle Two in emergencies.'[3]

The work was to be carried out during the ship's next yard period. Cassady estimated that it would add 820lbs to the ship's weight. However, the work was never done because ComServPac refused the request because:

> '(a) It requires additional weight on a ship that is already dangerously overweight and,
>
> '(b) although desirable, it is not considered an urgent military necessity.'[4]

The Circular of Requirements Process

As the 'Lexingtons' approached their tenth birthday, they could no longer be considered new ships. As was reasonable for major combatants nearing middle age, the US Navy began to consider reconstruction to correct major deficiencies that had failed to be addressed by the ShipAlt process.[5] The CNO instructed BuCon to establish the scope of work for the planned reconstruction of the 'Lexingtons'. The resulting document was the 'Circular of Requirements for the Modernization of the USS *Lexington* and USS *Saratoga*'.[6] This massive document was intended to be debated

among the bureaux and then submitted to Congress together with a cost estimate for a funding decision. Money for such reconstructions was not part of the Navy's regular ship maintenance budget and required a specific funding decision by a notoriously parsimonious Congress. The result was that, instead of the relatively short reaction cycle for ShipAlt improvements, where a change, if approved and funded, would generally be implemented within a year of the original request, this rebuilding cycle began in 1937 and resulted in the scheduling of the work for late 1939 or early the following year.

The Modernization of the 'Lexingtons'

In the first few years after their commissioning, the 'Lexingtons' needed very few changes; the only visible alterations were to the flight deck. Even minor structural differences between the ships were few prior to 1935 and most of these dated back to the their original construction. For example, the foremast radio compass booths on the two ships were different in shape and size: *Saratoga*'s had windows while *Lexington*'s did not. The searchlight platforms on the bridges of

Above: The secondary conning station and, above it, the open Pri-Fly were located on the forward face of the funnel, *Lexington*, 20 December 1927. Four small 6pdr saluting guns were located on a platform below these positions. Note the opening for the small aft elevator. (NARA)

the two ships were fitted in slightly different positions. The funnel searchlight platforms were carried a half level higher on *Lexington* than on *Saratoga* and the latter had a catwalk along the inboard face of the funnel while *Lexington* did not. Apart from these minor differences, the ships were externally identical in their first years.

Soon after their launch, both ships added structures at the flag bridge level, on the roof of the charthouse. A radio cabin was added on both ships between the after legs of the tripod foremast during their post-trials refit in the late summer of 1928. During these refits, both ships had a narrow walkway added at the flag bridge level around the pilot-house/chart-house roof, connecting with the lower searchlight platform. *Lexington* had a simple railing built up around the edge of this walkway; it was normally covered with canvas along the sides to provide weather protection. *Saratoga* had a more elaborate steel bulkhead added in early 1929 and this provided some splinter protection. The bulkhead was splayed outward in front to allow the rotation of the main battery rangefinder. *Lexington* replaced her railing with a similar splinter shield later in 1929. During the next five years, there were few further changes, apart from an extension to *Saratoga*'s flag bridge structures. During 1933 a flag plot compartment

was built on the pilot-house roof; the main battery rangefinder, formerly at that level, was moved to the roof of the new structure. To allow room for the rangefinder, the radio compass booth suspended from the lower top was deleted.

This stable period came to an end in 1935 when *Lexington* underwent a major upgrade to her AA armament. This involved the installation of four hull sponsons and a platform encircling the funnel at level five. The hull sponsons were located one at each bow and quarter at main deck level. Each was intended to mount four .50cal machine-guns. The funnel platform held six of these guns on each side and had searchlights mounted at each corner. The existing searchlight platforms and catwalk on *Lexington*'s funnel were eliminated. It was planned that similar changes, with minor modifications, would be made to *Saratoga* at her next yard period.[7] In the event, *Saratoga*'s modifications were repeatedly postponed, and the presence of these platforms on *Lexington* would be a distinguishing feature.

In 1936 an even more substantial change was made to *Lexington* with the widening of her flight deck forward. The 'Lexingtons'' turbo-electric drive allowed the ships to make the same speed aft as forward. This led to the conclusion that widening the flight deck forward

Right: *Saratoga* passing through the Gaillard Cut of the Panama Canal on 5 April 1931. The observation post suspended above the flight deck was used to con the ship through the canal; the off-centre island was felt to provide an inadequate view of the port side. A splinter shield has been added to the roof of the pilot-house, protecting the flag bridge level. (NARA)

Left: *Saratoga* sometime after 1932. Flag radio and flag plot compartments were built on the pilot-house roof and the main battery rangefinder moved up to the roof of flag plot. This necessitated the removal of the radio compass booth suspended from lower control top; it was not considered a serious loss since the DF loop located there never worked properly. Note the raised flight deck palisades. (NARA)

Below: A view of the rear of the foremast and funnel on *Saratoga* circa 1936. Note that the two control stations on the funnel were open to the weather in the rear. The box-like structures at the aft end of the navigation bridge were containers for signal flags.

and the addition of another complete set of arrester gear and barriers would permit the recovery of aircraft over the bow. This was envisaged as an emergency capability to be used only if the flight deck aft was damaged. As before, *Saratoga* was supposed to receive the widened flight deck at her next refit, but once again the change was postponed. This time, however, it was because it was now planned to undertake a complete stem-to-stern modernization of the 'Lexingtons', and it was assumed that this change and the delayed AA upgrades would be included. In August 1937 the CNO, at the recommendation of the General Board, initiated the planning for a major reconstruction of the 'Lexingtons'. The resulting 'Circular of Requirements' developed by BuCon, and delivered to the General Board in August 1938, listed the set of recommended changes, organized into the following 24 groups:[8]

Group I – General overhaul main propulsion machinery and auxiliaries – As the name implied, a refurbishing of the propulsion equipment plus minor incidental work, such as the installation of additional air compressors.

Group II – Completion of bomb and torpedo handling and stowage (*Saratoga* only) – Mainly minor work, already done in *Lexington*, to enlarge and in some cases relocate the bomb and torpedo magazines. It also included adding the bomb elevator forward of the forward

Right: In 1935 *Lexington* was taken in hand and new AA platforms were added to each bow and quarter and around the top level of her funnel. Taken at NY Puget Sound on 25 September 1925, this dockyard photograph shows details of the port forward platform. At the extreme right can be seen the folding extension added to the 5in sponson. (NARA)

Right: This view of *Lexington* taken on the same day as the previous picture shows the port aft AA platform and the funnel platform. The presence of extensive scaffolding indicates that work was still in progress. Note the LSO position right aft and the DF loop (actually a square) on its folding arm. (NARA)

aircraft elevator, also already done in *Lexington*.

Group III – Installation of blister – This was probably the single most important of the proposed changes. The instability inherent in the 'Lexingtons'' design was finally to be addressed [see Chapter 3]. It had been known since the ships were designed that adding the massive island and funnel structures to a symmetrical hull would build in an inherent starboard list that could be corrected only by uneven liquid loadings or by the addition of a

buoyancy blister on the starboard side. This second option, long discussed, was now to be implemented.

Group IV – Increase in AA machine-gun battery – Both ships were to get four 1.1in quadruple mgs and *Saratoga* was to get 23 additional .50cal mgs to bring her up to a total of 28, the same as *Lexington*. The necessary magazines, handling equipment and water-cooling piping were to be installed.

Group V – Provide machine-gun ammunition

for the .50cal AA guns and the 1.1in guns – All structural work for this was covered by the previous group.

Group VI – Widening flight deck forward and installation of forward arrester gear (*Saratoga* only) – Despite the name, this group actually covered only the widening of the flight deck. The plan was to give *Saratoga* a forward flight deck identical in size to *Lexington*'s but with substantially improved strength and better fairing. This work included the alteration of the emergency radio aerials in way of the widened flight deck.

Group VII – Modernization of present arrester gear and barriers (both vessels) and installation of forward arrester gear (*Saratoga* only) – *Saratoga* would receive a complete set of arrester gear forward; *Lexington*'s forward gear would have obsolescent mechanical elements replaced by current units. An amidships emergency set of arrester wires and barriers was to be fitted on both ships, and the after gear was to be modernized in the same way as *Lexington*'s forward gear.

Group VIII – Enlarge after elevator and speed up both elevators – An entirely new enlarged after elevator was to be fitted; the forward elevator mechanism was to be modified by enlarging the elevator platform and/or speeding up its operating cycle. *Lexington*'s torpedo elevator would have to be relocated to accommodate the new aft elevator; *Saratoga*, which had not yet received a torpedo elevator, was to have one installed in the correct location.

Group IX – Modernization of radio and sound equipment – This group encompassed the installation of new radio equipment, direction finders and the replacement of the obsolete 12in and 24in signal searchlights.

Group X – Improve island structure – This envisaged considerable rebuilding and enlargement of the island to provide more room for ship operating personnel, for air radio and for aviation ready rooms. The latter were to be located in a new enclosure to be built between the existing island and funnel. The plan also included the deletion of the existing Pri-Fly and secondary conning station on the forward end of the funnel. The work in this group included the addition of STS splinter shields at all bridge levels.

Group XI – Miscellaneous improvements to flight deck – The life netting around the edge of the flight deck was to be replaced by a light structural walkway, 3ft in width, positioned 4ft 6in below the deck edge, similar in nature to the

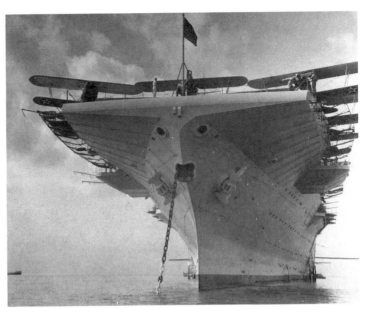

gallery deck structure installed on the new 'Yorktowns'.

Group XII – Additional outlets to flight deck – A general rearrangement and increase in the number and capacity of the avgas outlets at flight deck level to speed refuelling operations. The lubricating oil system was to be modified to allow a second grade of oil to be available as more modern aircraft used a heavier grade.

Group XIII – Installation of interior control announcing system flight deck and completion of sound-powered telephone project – This involved completion of a number of ongoing projects related to internal communications.

Group XIV – Lengthen flight deck aft – The flight deck was to be extended by a total of 16ft, but since the extension was to have only a very short round-down in place of the long ramp then in place, the change would add almost 30ft of usable space to the flight deck. The space inside the extended flight deck structure was to be used for the storage of smoke tanks.

Group XV – Compartmentation and damage control including gas defence – Ventilation closures, motor controls and counterflooding were all to be upgraded. Damage control facilities were to be brought up to contemporary standards as far as possible.

Group XVa – Installation of fuel oil system heating coils and make necessary changes in system to facilitate shifting oil for damage control purposes – BuEng was actually proposing an upgrading of the existing recirculating system.

Group XVI – Searchlights, installation remote

Above: In 1938 *Lexington*'s flight deck was widened forward to allow aircraft to be retrieved over the bow. The bow AA platforms were retained; the fairing supporting the flight deck was simply added forward of the platforms. (NARA)

Above: *Saratoga's* bow was similarly modified but not until 1941. This rare shot shows her as she appeared between August 1941 and January 1942, when she had both the widened bow and her original main battery. She has also had extra AA sponsons added forward, although very different ones from those added to *Lexington* in 1935. These were individual guntubs holding 3in AA guns, which were replaced in November 1941 with quad 1.1in machine-guns. (NARA)

control – Two remotely controlled searchlights were to be mounted on new platforms to be installed on the port face of the funnel.

Group XVII – Installation of two catapults – A pair of the latest model of catapult were to be fitted into the flight deck forward. On *Saratoga* only, this work included the removal of all vestiges of the original, long-unused fly-wheel catapult; that work had already been done on *Lexington* when her bow was widened.

Group XVIII – Purchase and installation of self-synchronous alidades and miscellaneous navigational instruments – Up-to-date navigational instruments were to be acquired and installed in the place of the obsolescent original equipment.

Group XIX – Installation of two 850kW diesel generators, switchboards and wiring – This work involved the proposed installation of two additional generators. BuCon expressed considerable doubt whether this work would be done, both because of the difficulty of finding space for new major equipment and because BuEng had expressed the opinion that the required electrical power could be better supplied by increasing the output of the existing generators than by adding new ones.

Group XX – Improvement of 5in AA battery including installation of remote control – The twelve existing 5in/25 AA mountings were to be fitted with the latest controls, including remote control training and aiming linked to two new Mk 33 directors.

Group XXI – Improve living quarters (rearrangement and ventilation sick bay and living quarters) – This group of improvements covered ventilation of the ship in general and sick bay in particular.

Group XXII – Hangar alterations – The hangar was to be extended aft from its present aft bulkhead at Frame 173 to at least Frame 177. This change would have added only about 15ft to the length of the hangar. A larger extension was mooted but would have meant the deletion of a significant proportion of the aviation shop areas, a move which BuCon thought inadvisable.

Group XXIII – Miscellaneous alterations to ventilation and insulation – This was a 'catch-all' group covering improvements to fire fighting equipment, berthing, messing and sanitation. This included adding a CO_2 smothering system for the paint shop and adding lavatory drains to officer's staterooms not already fitted with such drains.

Group XXIV – Installation of one 200kW diesel generator, switchboard and wiring – Like Group XIX, this called for the addition of more electrical power, and like that group, it was far from certain that the best solution was the addition of a new generator rather than the upgrading of the existing ones, in this case the lighting motor generators.

This list of proposed changes was intended to be the starting point for a process of debate and planning that would lead to estimates of cost in sufficient detail to generate a request for appropriation of funds by Congress.[9] In June 1939 Congress appropriated $15 million to cover the proposed changes, only $500,000 less than the original request.

The 'Lexingtons' were each scheduled to begin an eleven month yard period at Puget Sound Navy Yard, but even though the plans were now firm and the necessary money was available, the reconstructions would once again be postponed - due this time to the international situation. In September 1939 war broke out in Europe and even though officially the US remained neutral, no one in the US Navy really believed that this war would not inevitably involve the US as well. With that in mind, it seemed risky to tie up at least a quarter of the Navy's aircraft-carrier assets for a long period of time.[10] The logical solution was to divide up the planned yard periods; by January 1940 it had been decided to split the work into two shorter periods for each ship.[11] The first period, of six months, was to accomplish the most critical of the planned modifications: the installation of the starboard blister (Group III) and the elevator modifications (Group VIII). The only other work to be performed during this period was that which would not delay the scheduled completion. On 16 September 1940 definite dates for *Saratoga*'s first yard period were set for 6 January to 4 July 1941. However, this schedule would slip again because the contractors working on the new aft elevator and the modified forward elevator both experienced schedule delays. Finally the CNO intervened because, in his opinion, even the shortened yard periods envisaged in the latest plan were too long:

'The proposed schedule of modernization of *Lexington* and *Saratoga*... are hereby indefinitely deferred and availabilities for the work previously authorized are cancelled.

'*Saratoga* will be given a regular three-month overhaul period commencing 6 January 1941, and *Lexington* will be given a regular three-month overhaul period at the end of the usual 21 month interval for the overhaul of capital ships, i.e., commencing about May 1942.'[12]

The work on *Saratoga* was finally begun later than scheduled even after this last delay; it was completed only on 15 August 1941. The most significant changes were to the main deck and above. Sponsons for 3in/50 AA guns somewhat similar to those added to *Lexington* were added to each bow and quarter and these sponsons and the existing 5in gun emplacements were given STS splinter shielding. An emergency battle dressing station was created on the main deck on the starboard side directly below the island. The flight deck was widened forward and extended aft. A radio direction finder (radio compass) compartment was added to the forward edge of the bridge structure at flag bridge level. AA guns and a radio transmitter station were added on the roof of the flag bridge structures. AA guns were also added to the structures on the aft face of the funnel at the level of the main battery director. A CXAM air search radar was added to the forward lip of the funnel and the secondary conning station and Pri-Fly on the forward face of the funnel were replaced by a radar control station for the CXAM.[13]

Saratoga re-entered the yard at Puget Sound for a period of 'restricted availability' only days after this last overhaul had been completed. When she emerged in late November 1941, she had still further changes, including the replacement of her recently added 3in/50 AA guns by 1.1in twin AA machine-guns. An FC radar was added to the forward and aft upper

tops immediately behind the 5in directors. A catwalk was added from the navigation bridge level of the island to the new CXAM control station on the forward face of the funnel.[14]

Lexington also had some minor work done shortly before the war at Pearl Harbor. She had a CXAM radar added to the forward lip of her funnel, probably in June 1941, almost identical to *Saratoga*'s installation except that, due to fears expressed by Halsey that funnel gases and whistle steam would interfere with the radar aerial in this location,[15] a cap was added to the foremost funnel uptake, directing the hot gases aft. Also, like *Saratoga*, she had the control room for the CXAM built up on the forward face of the funnel in place of the secondary conning station and the Pri-Fly; in addition, the catwalk was added between her bridge and funnel, although this was probably not done until August 1941.

Below: *Lexington* had her main battery removed after *Saratoga*, although both were done at Pearl Harbor and both were given to the Army for coast defence in Hawaii. This view, on 30 March 1942, shows the removal of No. 3 8in mounting, No. 4 having already been removed. Note that the aft main battery control top is already being modified; with the main battery removed, there was no need for a main battery director. Note also the splinter mats erected around the aft control tops and the funnel AA platform. (NARA)

Below: After being
torpedoed in January 1942,
Saratoga entered NY Puget
Sound for extensive repairs
and a long-overdue refit,
including the addition of the
starboard stability blister
and the cutting down of her
foremast and funnel. Note
the twin 5in gunhouses aft of
the funnel and the 1.1in
quad forward. Mk 37
directors with FD radar
have been added to control
her beefed-up heavy AA
battery, 14 May 1942.
(NARA)

Lexington received extra AA guns at the aft end of the funnel and replaced the 3in/50 mountings on each of her four corner sponsons with a quadruple 1.1in mounting at the same time. She also received the new YE aircraft homing beacon.[16]

This, then, was the general state of the 'Lexingtons' at the outbreak of war. The CNO acknowledged that there was a long list of overdue upgrades to these ships, but, in accordance with a general order dated 18 December 1941, all scheduled overhauls for ships of the Pacific Fleet were held in abeyance.[17] He ordered Puget Sound to prepare to perform necessary alterations when the ships became available. The list included most of the outstanding items from the 'Circular of Requirements'. New items on the list included completion of alterations to the AA battery by

replacing all .50cal machine-guns by the newly favoured light AA weapon, the 20mm Oerlikon, and the addition of power drives and directors for all the recently installed 1.1in medium AA guns. Other new items included the installation of a flight deck announcing system and the permanent degaussing of *Lexington*.

Lexington had been fitted with a temporary degaussing installation in 1941.[18] The emergence of the effective magnetic detonator and the extensive use by the Germans of magnetic mines off the coast of Britain led the US Navy hastily to install degaussing equipment in its capital ships. The temporary installation was a 213-volt system using three interlocking coils, designated M, F and Q. Considerable trouble had been experienced keeping the system operational because the coils had been run along the external shell plating where they

were protected only by canvas covers.[19] The permanent installation was intended to solve these problems by running the coils inside the shell plating.[20] The M coil ran the length of the ship at various levels with two crossovers near the bow. The F coil was actually two separate loops that ran at flight deck level near the bow. The Q coil was similar except that it was located near the stern and comprised three rather than two loops. A fourth coil, the A coil, was designed to run in diagonals back and forth across the ship from bow to stern.

The CNO directive authorizing the completion of the modernization of the 'Lexingtons' had specifically ordered that the changes were to be made only when the ships were available.[21] In the case of *Saratoga*, the Japanese would soon provide her with the spare time she needed to carry out most of the overdue upgrades - she was torpedoed by the submarine *I-6* on 11 January 1942 near Pearl Harbor. The damage was not serious but was

sufficient to require her immediate docking. Passing through Pearl Harbor on her way to Puget Sound, her 8in main battery was removed.[22] Once at Bremerton, she was docked and, in addition to the repair of the torpedo damage, the long-planned starboard stability blister was installed.[23] A number of other major structural changes were made during this yard period including the removal of *Saratoga*'s tripod foremast, which was replaced by a light pole mast. The air lookout station formerly sited on her upper foretop (known as Sky Forward) was relocated to the roof of the flag bridge, which was turned into a third bridge level with wind and splinter shielding but, significantly, no overhead cover.[24] The foremast was deleted primarily to save weight but also because space had to be found on the island for the new forward 5in director. The 5in battery was significantly modified by the removal of all twelve 5in/25 mountings which were replaced by sixteen of the far more effective 5in/38s. The

Above and left: These two photographs, both starboard broadside views, show *Lexington* in 1934 and *Saratoga* after her Spring 1942 refit. The most obvious differences are the main battery, replaced by 5in twin gunhouses, and the foremast which has been cut down. Less obvious is the reduction in height by one level of the funnel. Note also the extension of the flight deck aft.(NARA)

Right: After being torpedoed again in August 1942, *Saratoga* emerged from her repairs with a significantly strengthened light AA fit, as evidenced by the many 20mm guntubs now lining the port side of her flight deck. (NARA)

medium and light AA batteries were also upgraded by the addition of four twin 1.1in mountings and the replacement of all .50cal machine-guns by 20mm Oerlikons. *Saratoga's* radar suite was augmented by the addition of a second air search set, a sea search set and fire control radar for the two new Mk 37 directors. Finally, in a further weight-reduction move, the height of the funnel was reduced by 20ft to approximately 59ft.[25]

With *Saratoga* out of the war for the immediate future, *Lexington* had no opportunity to schedule her own long-overdue reconstruction. The best that she could do was a short visit to the yard at Pearl Harbor in late March 1942, when it was planned to extend her flag bridge structures to resemble *Saratoga's* (as they looked prior to her 1942 rebuild). *Lexington* did not like the fact *Saratoga's* flag bridge walkway was exposed to the weather; *Lexington* wanted the entire structure enclosed by STS and shatterproof glass.[26] BuShips' only comment was that the work was to proceed on a 'not to delay basis'.[27] The major change made at Pearl Harbor was the removal of her main battery. Like *Saratoga's* 8in mountings, they were desired by the Army command in Hawaii as coastal defence batteries. Unlike *Saratoga*, there was neither the time nor the material to replace the 8in mountings with 5in gunhouses. Instead, *Lexington* received three additional 1.1in quadruple mountings in place of the forward superfiring and two after mountings. It was in this condition that *Lexington* was lost at

the Battle of the Coral Sea. Detailed plans existed to complete her modernization: she would have emerged from her next refit looking almost identical to *Saratoga*, as she appeared in late May 1942 on completion of her reconstruction.[28]

Saratoga emerged from Puget Sound just too late to participate in the pivotal Battle of Midway, but was embroiled in the Solomons Campaign from its beginning on 7 August 1942. It was there that she was torpedoed again, this time by the submarine *I-26* on 31 August. Once again she headed back to Pearl Harbor, but little work was done there apart from patching up the hole in her side and augmenting her light and medium AA fits, the former by adding more mountings, the latter by replacing all 1.1in guns by new 40mm Bofors quadruple mountings.[29]

Saratoga's next yard period was a regularly scheduled overhaul starting in late November 1943. She had managed to survive 1943 without damage and in view of the rate at which electronics and armament had evolved since November 1942, she was seriously in need of a refit. In preparation, BuShips again studied the 1938 'Circular of Requirements' to determine which items had been completed, which had been overtaken by events and which still awaited completion. In fact, very few of the original requirements fell into the last category. Most, like the stability blister (Group III), had already been completed or, like the enlargement of the hangar (Group XXII), had been cancelled because the improvement to be

gained seemed incommensurate with the cost in time and money.[30] The few major items still on the list to be accomplished included the elevator work (Group VII) and the addition of flight deck catapults (Group XVII).

Saratoga emerged from the Navy Yard at Hunters Point in January 1944. The work done there was mainly concerned with upgrading her AA fit and, apart from a minor upgrading of her electronics, few other changes were made. She was therefore in the yard again, this time at Puget Sound, between June and September 1944 for another round of modernization.[31] This included a complete renovation of her electronics and the replacement of her forward elevator machinery by new, faster equipment, but the enlarged platform that was to have accompanied that change was still unavailable. In an attempt to save topweight, to compensate in part for the added radar aerials, *Saratoga*'s conning tower armour was removed. Two forward catapults were added and all traces of her forward arrester gear were removed.[32] Her remaining arrester gear was upgraded. Her inert gas system was replaced by a new one and the small makeshift CIC was replaced by a much larger space on the main deck. Finally, she received a distinctive disruptive camouflage pattern.

Saratoga began working up air groups in the Hawaii area in her new role as a night carrier. Before rejoining the fleet, she had a brief yard visit at Pearl Harbor between 1 and 8 November 1944 during which her bright camouflage was painted out, and again between 31 December 1944 and 10 January 1945 when night landing lights and electronic beacons were installed.[33] Within a fortnight she was again damaged by enemy action: Kamikaze attack

tore up her flight deck forward and sent her back to Puget Sound. In view of *Saratoga*'s age and her increasing difficulty in handling the new generation of naval aircraft, it was decided not to return her to full combat status.[34] She was now to be used as a training carrier and would spend her nights in port. To suit this new role, part of her hangar deck was converted into enclosed compartments to serve as classrooms and, since her aft elevator was no longer needed, the elevator shaft was plated over and the platform and machinery removed. As partial compensation for the loss of her aft elevator, the long-overdue enlarged platform for her forward elevator was installed. The night landing lights installed just months before were removed.

These last modifications served *Saratoga* well during her last official duty, carrying returning servicemen home from Hawaii as part of Operation 'Magic Carpet'. While engaged in this duty, she suffered storm damage to the port forward AA sponson. Rather than repair the damage it was decided to delete the foremost sponsons on both sides.[35] Sometime before February 1946 additional AA guns were deleted from *Saratoga* in an attempt to increase her stability by reducing topweight. Approximately half her AA guns of all calibres, including two of her twin 5in gunhouses, were removed.

1. GenBd, BuCon -> GenBd, 6 March 1926, Airplane Carriers, p 18. This report from BuCon stated that the four kedge anchors were being added to the design and questioned the need for four anchors at the stern. I&S, 4 November 1931, Report of Material Inspection of U.S.S. *Lexington* (CV2), p 26. This inspection found the kedge anchors unnecessary: 'These anchors are not needed and should be removed'.

2. ibid, p 71.

3. BuShips, Sara -> BuShips, 10 June 1944, U.S.S. *Saratoga* (CV3) - Alteration Request No. 26-44 (Extension of

Above: After an early 1944 refit at NY Hunters Point, *Saratoga* now carried many fewer 20mm guns but a greatly increased battery of 40mm Bofors, 16 June 1944. Note the larger sponsons needed for these bigger guns along her flight deck forward and in each of the port side boat pockets. (NARA)

catwalk from Bridge to Secondary Control Platform).

4. BuShips, ComServPac -> BuShips, 26 June 1944, U.S.S. *Saratoga* (CV3) - Alteration Request No. 26-44 (Extension of catwalk from Bridge to Secondary Control Platform) (1st Endorsement).

5. This process has been recreated for contemporary USN aircraft-carriers; SLEP (Service Life Extension Programme) was invented to allow major rejuvenation of these carriers in their middle age to allow them to exceed their nominal 30-year life span by an additional 50 per cent (see US CVs, p 267).

6. BuCon, undated, Circular of Requirements for the Modernization of the USS *Lexington* and USS *Saratoga* for work under the Cognizance of the Bureau of Construction & Repair. While undated, this document can be placed fairly accurately as the late summer of 1938; the latest reference with the document is 9 August 1938.

7. BuCon, NYPS -> BuCon, 27 September 1935, USS *Saratoga* (CV3) - .50 Caliber A. A. Machine-gun Installation - Platforms on each bow and quarter - Change in design.

8. BuCon, undated, Circular of Requirements for the Modernization of the USS *Lexington* and USS *Saratoga* for work under the Cognizance of the Bureau of Construction & Repair. Despite the title, this document listed the work to be done by all bureaux.

9. op.cit. The preface to the 'Circular of Requirements' states: 'The requirements listed herein are not considered complete but sufficient to permit Puget Sound Yard to proceed with the preliminary work of preparation of Detail Specifications and sketch plans (similar to those furnished for new construction) and the preparation of estimates of weight and cost as stated in the letter forwarding this circular.'

10. At this time, the US Navy had five aircraft-carriers (*Lexington*, *Saratoga*, *Ranger*, *Yorktown* and *Enterprise*) but, with war in Europe, it had to split its focus between two oceans and *Ranger* was considered too small to be counted on for combat operations.

11. BuShips, NYPS -> BuShips, 16 September 1940, USS *Saratoga* (CV3) - Modernization - Commencement of First Period. The decision to split the yard periods was made in a series of letters between October 1939 and January 1940. This letter was mainly to report continuing delays in the preparations for the planned elevator work.

12. BuShips, CNO -> BuShips, 23 October 1940, USS *Lexington* and USS *Saratoga* - Modernization - Deferring

13. The source for this set of changes and those completed in November 1941 is a list on the back sheet of a set of BuShips plans of *Saratoga* dated 1944.

14. BuShips, ComAirBatFor -> BuShips, 29 March 1941, Naval Message 292253. This was a request for authority to install a catwalk on both 'Lexingtons' between the bridge and the funnel. BuShips, BuShips -> NYPS, 17 April 41, Naval Message 172200. This replying dispatch authorized NYPS to perform this work on *Saratoga* and NYPH to modify *Lexington*.

15. BuShips, ComAirBatFor -> BuShips, 2 January 41, CXAM Equipment - Installation of. Halsey suggested that the CXAM be located on the foremast above and behind the upper top.

16. I&S, , 5 September 41, U.S.S. *Lexington* (CV2) - Material Inspection of, p IV-3. The CXAM and YE installations were listed as items added to *Lexington* since her last inspection.

17. BuShips, CNO -> NYPS, 1 January 42, U.S.S. *Lexington* (CV2) and U.S.S. *Saratoga* (CV3) - Modernization. The 18 December 1941 order from the CNO is referenced in this document.

18. BuShips, , 19 January 1942, Degaussing - Coil Section: Maintenance Inspection. This document dates *Lexington*'s first degaussing calibration as 4 April 41 at Maui.

19. ibid. Heavy seas had ripped the M and F coils loose from the bow on more than one occasion. Oil and water lighters had caused breaks or grounds just by bumping up against the ship's side during normal replenishment operations.

20. BuShips, , 9 January 42, Specifications for Permanent Degaussing Installations on U.S.S. *Lexington* (CV2) AND U.S.S. *Saratoga* (CV3). The author has found no documentation that indicates whether this planned work was actually carried out on either ship.

21. BuShips, CNO -> NYPS, 1 January 42, U.S.S. *Lexington* (CV2) and U.S.S. *Saratoga* (CV3) - Modernization.

22. BuShips, , 16 June 42, Interview of Commander Alfred M. Pride, USN, in the Bureau of Aeronautics, p 6.:

23. BuShips, BuShips -> NYPS, 12 February 42, U.S.S. *Saratoga* (CV3) - Alterations Authorized for Coming Overhaul. Since this was a list of planned modifications rather than a list of completed modifications, the

Right: After sustaining a Kamikaze attack off Iwo Jima, *Saratoga* effectively retired from the war. She was now used as a training carrier and, after the end of hostilities, as a transport carrying troops home from the Pacific. This 11 October 1945 view shows her flight deck crowded with some of her cargo of returning veterans. (NARA)

completion of all changes mentioned in this document cannot be assumed.

24. The US Navy listened to advice from the Royal Navy on this point, which had found that an open bridge was essential for sky lookout.

25. BuShips, BuAer -> BuShips, 1 January 1942, Recommended Reduction of Weight and Improvement of Military Characteristics - U.S.S. *Saratoga* (8th Endorsement).

26. BuShips, , 28 March 1942, *Lexington* Repair Request, No. 7-42.

27. BuShips, NYPH -> NYPS, 30 March 1942, . Pearl Harbor's only concern was that the changes to *Lexington*'s flag bridge would not interfere with the future mounting of Mk 37 directors. The evidence as to whether the desired changes were made to *Lexington*'s flag bridge is sparse, but seems to indicate that she had an enclosed flag bridge at the time of her loss.

28. BuShips, BuShips -> Lex, 20 May 1942, USS *Lexington* (CV2) - Alterations Authorized. The fact that this document dates from after *Lexington*'s loss indicates nothing more than the tendency of bureaucracies to grind on in the face of reality.

29. BuShips, NYPH -> BuShips, 10 November 1942, USS *Saratoga* (CV3) - Weight Changes Incidental to Armament Alterations.

30. BuShips, BuShips -> NYPS, 21 December 1943, U.S.S. *Saratoga* (CV3) - Status of Modernization Items, Bureau's Action on.

31. BuShips, This is the NYPS departure report on *Saratoga*. It is undated but shows *Saratoga* leaving the yard on 8 September 1944.

32. The arrester wires, but not the mechanical elements, were deleted by the ship's company sometime during 1943.

33. BuShips, 10 August 1945, . Despite the date on this document, it is in fact the NYPH departure report for *Saratoga* for her yard period between 31 December 1944 and 10 January 1945.

34. BuShips, NYPS Departure Report.

35. BuShips, Sara -> CinCUS, 11 November 1945, Hull Damage -Report of.

2.2 Propulsion

The 'Lexington'-class was equipped with turbo-electric propulsion, a system favoured by the US Navy in the years during and immediately after the First World War. The development of steam propulsion systems for major warships from the middle of the 19th century had stepped rapidly through increasingly efficient means of turning the energy of steam into movement for a ship. The revolutionary HMS *Dreadnought* of 1907 had made turbines the standard means of steam propulsion, because they were smaller, more reliable and more powerful than the reciprocating engines they supplanted. However, turbines had their problems, the main one being that they could operate with maximum efficiency at only one speed. Decisions regarding the number of stages of turbine blades and the size, shape and angle of those blades locked that optimal speed into the turbine's design. And, since capital ships all used speed to gain tactical advantage, capital ship turbines tended to be designed to operate best at high speeds. This had the disadvantage of making most turbine-powered warships inefficient steamers at cruising speed. Operating the high-speed turbines at lower power, and therefore speed, was like running a motor car at low speed in high gear. One recourse was to provide a separate set of cruising turbines optimized for slower speed. Even worse, to reverse the screws required yet another set of turbines.

The introduction of geared turbines offered a solution to this increasing complexity, but they were just coming into use at the time the 'Lexingtons' were being designed.[1] Gearing added flexibility to a ship's powerplant; turbines could be run at their most efficient speed and torque, and the rate and direction of rotation of the propeller shafts adjusted to the needs of the moment. This gearing, like a car's transmission, was complex and the reliability of the heavy gearing required by ship's turbines was still far from proven. Also, it required that the turbines be run at full power even when less than full speed was needed - an extremely wasteful and inefficient arrangement. The only expedient was to shut down whole sets of boilers, turbines and shafts. In the design of the 'New Mexico'-class battleships laid down in 1915, the US Navy's warship designers had opted instead for a turbo-electric drive that separated the generation of kinetic energy (in the form of a rotating turbine core) from the actual propulsion of the ships (in the form of a rotating propeller shaft), not by gearing but by a system of electrical power generation and use.

The steam turbines in a turbo-electric system drove electrical generators instead of directly driving the ship's screws or indirectly driving them through gearing. The generated electricity was directed by a control panel into drive motors attached to the propeller shafts. The advantages of this arrangement over either of the conventional turbine systems were several.[2] All gearing and extra turbine sets were unnecessary because all direction and speed control came from the control panel. In theory at least, turbo-electric systems were far more resistant to damage because they allowed greater internal subdivision of the machinery spaces and, because of the ease with which electricity could be switched around, the loss of boilers or generators to accident or damage could be handled with far greater facility; it would take a casualty to the drive motors themselves to prevent a propeller shaft from receiving power. The system could be run at any level of power generation, meaning that a set of boilers and turbo-generators could be shut down and all motors powered off the on-line generators. The disadvantages seemed to be relatively minor. A turbo-electric system was bigger, heavier and costlier than an equivalent geared turbine system. It was also less efficient, losing up to 10 per cent of input energy to heat, friction and electrical resistance, while a geared turbine system approached 99 per cent efficiency. The main problem with turbo-electric drive emerged only after some years of experience with the systems; no amount of insulation and protection proved sufficient to preclude electrical short circuits due to battle damage or shock. When a short circuit occurred, the currents involved were so high as to make repair work extremely dangerous for the engineering crews.

The penalties associated with turbo-electric drive were considered acceptable because the 'Lexingtons' were to be far bigger and more powerful than any warships previously built for the US Navy. The preceding 'Maryland'-class battleships had been fitted with a powerplant that produced approximately 29,000shp, giving a speed of 21kt. The planned 'South Dakota'-class battleships were to be significantly bigger and have a speed of 23kt, requiring a powerplant producing 60,000shp. The 'Lexingtons' were to have a speed of 33kt, requiring a powerplant of 180,000shp, three

times bigger than the biggest propulsion system planned by the US Navy and six times bigger than the biggest actually built. The only choice that the 'Lexingtons'' designers felt they could make was simply to extrapolate the known characteristics of the 'Marylands'' powerplants. The 'Lexingtons' would have a turbo-electrical propulsion system and it would be the biggest so far built.

The Engineering Plant

The 'Lexingtons' had sixteen boilers. In *Saratoga*, they were Babcock and Wilcox water-tube boilers of the White-Forster type, capable of producing steam at a working pressure of 295psi, while *Lexington* had Yarrow express-type small-tube boilers; all were oil-fired. Each boiler was in a separate fire room, eight to a side, located on the outside of the central machinery space. A set of four boilers, two to a side, fed their steam into a turbo-generator, of which there were four, taking up the central part of the machinery spaces. The steam was then routed into one of eight main condenser units, where it was cooled back into water and drained back into a feed water tank. The turbo-generators were thirteen-stage General Electric turbines each driving a three-phase revolving-field electrical alternator, also manufactured by GE. Each turbo-generator normally produced 35,200kW at a voltage of 4,980V; the maximum potential of each unit was 6,250V. These supplied the electrical power which, shunted

Below: In December 1928 *Lexington* was recruited by the city of Tacoma, WA, to provide electrical power, as its normal hydro-electric source was threatened due to a drought. Such was the power generation capability of these ships that she was able to provide sufficient power to run the city 12 hours a day for 30 days until the crisis had passed. During that period, she remained docked, power cables stretching from her boat pockets to a sub-station on shore. (NARA)

through the busbars at main control, was
directed to the pair of drive motors on each of
the four shafts. The drive motors were squirrel-
cage type, rotor-wound 5,000V units, designed
to be run on current ranging between 2,310 and
870A, producing between 22,500 and 5,000shp
each.[3] The drive motors could be configured to
use 22 or 44 poles, half or all of the electrical
rotors.

At maximum power, this added up to the
180,000shp total that drove the ships at
approximately 33kt. This speed was seldom
needed; any extended operations at that speed
would put far too much stress on the
engineering plant and would burn fuel at an
exorbitant rate. It was far more common to run
at cruising speed, which was approximately
16kt. When running at this speed, it was normal
to shut down part of the system, from boilers to
drive motors, for maintenance or as reserve
units in case of damage; steam would then be
supplied to only two of the main turbo-
generators. When *Saratoga* was torpedoed on
31 August 1942, she was in typical cruising
configuration (engineering set-up No. 5) with
'Baker' and 'Cast' units (turbo-generators)
running, 'Dog' unit on 5 minutes' notice and
'Able' unit on 30 minutes' notice. Drive was
being supplied by the forward motor on each
shaft only. Boilers 1, 2, 5, 8, 10, 13 and 14 were
on line; boilers 6, 7, 9, 15 and 16 were shut
down; the rest were on stand-by.[4]

In addition to the main propulsion plant, six
turbo-generators were provided to produce
power for the ship's lighting and other needs.
These six units, three on each dynamo flat, were
also GE units and each produced 750kW at
3,125A and 230V. These units were also known
as 'exciters' because they provided the 125kW
of excitation required by each main generator.
To reduce this line voltage to the 120V needed
for the ship's lighting, there were four 125kW
GE motor generators, two each in the forward
and aft distribution rooms. Each consisted of a
230V electric motor driving a 120V generator.
Other motor generators were installed to
provide power of the correct characteristics for
IC, fire control (four 200kW sets which raised
the 230V line voltage to 440V three-phase to
power the ship's guns), degaussing and the
ship's radios.[5]

Normal operation was to keep only four of
the six exciters, two in each dynamo flat,
running at any one time. One of each pair
supplied excitation power to a main unit, while
the other supplied the ship's service load. The
distribution boards were isolated so that the

forward flat supplied power to the forward part of the ship and the after generator supplied aft. At GQ, the third turbo-generator in each flat was brought on line, primarily to supply power to the fire control motor generators.[6]

For emergencies, when the main powerplant was shut down, there were storage batteries capable of providing power to the ship's lights and other essential systems. In the event of power loss, three 60kW, 440V three-phase diesel generators were available to provide power to some of the guns. (These were only added to *Saratoga* during her early 1942 reconstruction; before that, batteries provided the only emergency power.) In 1944 these generators could supply just about enough power to keep the 40mm battery in operation.[7]

The Tacoma Incident

Soon after joining the fleet, *Lexington* had an opportunity to demonstrate an unexpected side benefit of turbo-electric drive. The Pacific North-West, particularly the city of Tacoma, Washington, was hard hit by drought in 1929. The worst side-effect was the failure of the city's hydro-electric power system due to insufficient water flow. The city authorities knew of the presence of *Lexington* and *Saratoga* at nearby Bremerton, where they were undergoing post-trials refits, and requested that one of the ships be made available as a floating electric power station for the duration of the crisis. The Navy was only too happy to oblige, so long as Tacoma put down a deposit covering the anticipated costs; it was charged at the rate of one cent per kilowatt-hour of delivered power.[8] *Lexington* docked at Tacoma on 15 December 1929 and began delivering power two days later. She delivered an average of 12,000kW for 12 hours each day for the next 30 days, allowing the city's reservoir to rebuild its water level to acceptable levels.[9]

Problems with Turbo-Electric Drive

The events that followed the torpedoing of *Saratoga* on 31 August 1942 are typical of the vulnerability of a turbo-electric drive system to battle damage. The following is extracted from the 'Engineering Narrative' attached to the Action Report:

'At 0748 August 31, 1942, when the U.S.S. *Saratoga* was hit by a torpedo the control equipment was on set-up No.5, "Baker" and "Cast" main generators, 44 poles split control. The torpedo hit the ship on the starboard side in the vicinity of frame 131 or 132 slightly forward of the Main Control space. When the

torpedo struck the ship, an instantaneous electrical explosion occurred behind the control board in the high-tension cell causing the field protective devices to function and disconnect the generators from the high-tension busbars[10]...The explosion was caused by an arc formed by the closing and opening of a normally opened high-tension bus switch which momentarily short-circuited the two generators in operation. The switch was designed to be shock-proof and remain in the open position but the terrific impact of the torpedo explosion caused severe strain to be set up in the mechanical support of the switch thereby allowing it to momentarily close. Power was immediately restored and operation was resumed. Prior to 0750 reports to Main Control from thrust blocks indicated damage to No.2 and No.3 shafts and at 0750 the motors on these shafts were disconnected. Power was off for disconnecting these motors and at 0752 when power was again applied "Baker" high-tension cell exploded due to electrical discharge over the previously carbonized electrical contacts and insulating supports causing "Baker" to be tripped off the line...At 0758 all engines stopped for electrical examination to prevent further trouble. At 0803 all motor rooms and thrust blocks are reported as satisfactory and ground neutrals are pulled and testing began immediately...At 0830 routine securing started for "Baker" unit. At 0830 main unit "Dog", which was idling on the bypass, was secured in order to repair a condenser which was reported as having a salinity of 15 grains...At 0836 on completion of electrical tests shifts were made from set-up No.5 to set-up No.1 with "Able" generator, which was warmed up after the securing of General Quarters, on No.4 shaft with forward and after motors, 44 poles, with no power on Nos. 1, 2 or 3 shafts. "Cast" unit was not put back on line at this time pending further electrical tests...At 1025 stop, brought generator "Cast" on line, 44 poles, No.1 shaft forward and after motors...At 1043 electrical explosion in "Baker" high-tension cell caused by increasing voltage due to increased speed of "Able" generator. The voltage caused electrical discharge on the carbonized paths on the bus ties located in "Baker" high-tension cell. At 1045 tripped "Able" by hand and took power off all shafts in order to remove all interconnecting bus ties on all four units to prevent a recurrence of the last electrical explosion.'[11]

After having slowed to a stop immediately after being torpedoed and then regaining power, *Saratoga* was now incapable of movement. She was taken under tow by the heavy cruiser *Minneapolis* at 1226; by 1310 the buss ties had been removed and *Saratoga* was able to resume power to her screws again, although it was 1637 before the tow was cast off. The next day, at 1043, 'Able' unit again tripped due to accumulated current leakage in its high-tension cell. It was found possible to continue in set-up No.1 by reducing the voltage through 'Able' cell to a safe level and compensating by running No.4 shaft's drive motors at 44 poles and reduced revolutions and handling the imbalance between shafts with the rudder. 'Baker' cell was finally repaired sufficiently to replace 'Able' by 1546 on 3 September and repairs then commenced on 'Able' cell. These repairs were completed at approximately 1000 on 4 September. Only then could the engineering plant report anything resembling normal capability, despite the fact that the total direct damage caused by the torpedo amounted to the flooding of one boiler room and the partial flooding of another.

1. HMS Furious, laid down in 1915, was the first Royal Navy capital ship with geared turbines.
2. BBs, p 218. This is a good general description of the advantages and disadvantages of turbo-electric propulsion.
3. I&S, 4 November 1931, Report of Material Inspection of U.S.S. *Lexington* (CV2) and I&S, , 1 July 1938, U.S.S. *Saratoga* (CV3) - Material Inspection of.
4. BuShips, Sara -> CinCUS, 10 September 1942, Action Report on Torpedoing of U.S.S. *Saratoga*, 31 August 1942.
5. BuShips, Sara -> BuShips, 8 February 1944, U.S.S. *Saratoga* (CV3) - Alteration Request No. 30-43.
6. BuShips, Sara -> BuShips, 28 February 1943, U.S.S. *Saratoga* (CV3) - Electrical Equipment- Ordering of.
7. op.cit. This request was for two additional diesel generators to provide emergency power for the 5in battery. Each of the three existing generators could power six 40mm mountings for approximately half an hour before it began to overheat. *Saratoga* felt that, with improved ventilation, each generator could service six or more mountings indefinitely.
8. BuCon, CNO -> Lex, 13 December 1929. There was also to be an additional charge based on the number of generators used and the city was to pay for fuel oil and all other consumables used above normal port rates.
9. Payne, Stephen A., The Carrier That Lit Up Tacoma, in Naval History, Vol. 4, No. 4, Fall 1990, Annapolis, MD.
10. Translated into English, that meant that a circuit-breaker tripped and the main units were no longer supplying power to the drive motors.
11. BuShips, Sara -> CinCUS, 10 September 1942, Action Report on Torpedoing of U.S.S. *Saratoga*, 31 August 1942.

2.3 Crew

The crew of the 'Lexingtons' varied in size considerably over the years. They were designed to be manned by 148 officers and 1,500 men.[1] In the years before the war, they rarely reached this complement because the

Left: The primary job of main control was the direction of the huge voltages generated by the main units to the drive motors in the right combination and at the right power levels. The banks of knife switches, circuit-breakers and busbars allowed fine control of the electrical set-up, *Saratoga*, 16 November 1944. (NARA)

Right: It may not have been elegant, but it worked! Rear Admiral W.A. Radford was transferred from the destroyer *Brown* (DD546) to *Saratoga* on 29 November 1943 by means of a canvas bag slung between the two ships. When in combat, *Saratoga* was usually a flagship, hosting the admiral in local tactical command. She was designed specifically for such duties and had appropriate accommodation on the main deck and a flag bridge level with its own plot and radio facilities. (NARA)

Far right: The CO looked little different from any of his senior officers, except that he was generally the only one aboard to hold the rank of captain and therefore wore the eagle insignia of that rank on his collars. This was *Saratoga*'s last CO, Captain Frank Akers, on the navigation bridge, one level below the flag bridge, his normal battle station. (NARA)

Left: *Saratoga*'s engineers pose as if inspecting the pair of huge drive motors connected to one of the ship's four propeller shafts. These motors converted the electrical power generated by the main units back into kinetic energy, in the form of a rotating propeller shaft, 16 November 1944. (NARA)

restricted budgets of the 1930s forced the Navy to choose between new construction and fully manned ships. Thus in 1931 *Lexington* was manned by 110 officers and 1,356 men.[2] By 1938 *Saratoga* was manned by only 79 officers and 1,354 men.[3] Wartime and the explosive increase in the number of AA weapons and electronic systems, however, would drive the number of officers and men far above the originally planned figure.

A roster of officers for *Saratoga* dated 1 December 1942 yields considerable data concerning the number and duties of the officers then assigned.[4] Commander TF11 (Rear Admiral DeWitt Ramsey) was on board at the time with his staff of twelve officers. The ship's officer corps was completely independent of the admiral and his staff and consisted of 102 line officers, five medical officers, two dental officers, four supply officers, one chaplain and three Marine officers – a total of 117 officers. The Commanding Officer was Captain Gerald Bogan; the remaining line officers included four commanders (including Commander Edgar Cruise, the XO), 10 lieutenant commanders, 27 lieutenants, 29 lieutenants junior grade and 31 ensigns. The ship's commissioned officers were divided by rank into two groups, the wardroom officers and the junior officers, based on where they messed; on *Saratoga*, the division was between lieutenants, who were considered wardroom officers, and lieutenant jgs and ensigns, who were considered junior officers. In addition to these commissioned officers, *Saratoga* also had 27 warrant officers, including three bosuns, four gunners, three electricians and eight machinists. While the CO did not have

a staff as such, he did have a group of senior officers who held responsibility for the major areas of ship's activities. These generally included the XO, air officer, navigator, communications officer, gunnery officer, first lieutenant (in charge of the ship's physical structure, in general, and damage control, in particular) and engineering officer.

The enlisted personnel were divided into three groups, by rating: seamen, petty officers and chief petty officers (CPOs). The higher rated petty officers and the CPOs represented the technical expertise of the Navy; they were career enlisted men whose accumulated experience kept the ship's systems working. (Officers served tours of duty that most often lasted less than two years; a good officer relied on his petty officers and chiefs to know how to solve most problems.) Exceptional CPOs could be promoted to warrant rank; in very rare cases, a chief or warrant officer would be commissioned.

The crew was organized in two distinctly different fashions. The enlisted men were divided into branches depending on specialization and the degree of training they had received. Thus, in 1938, *Saratoga*'s enlisted personnel was divided into the following branches: seamen 515; artificers 554; special 86; commissary 23; messmen 38; marines 85; and aviation 53 – to make the total of 1,354 crewmen then assigned.[5]

The other organization was by ship's divisions, which was based on the combat duty of the officers and men. Each of the 20 divisions was commanded by a division officer and, depending on its size, a number of junior

division officers, and was manned by an appropriate number of crewmen of the necessary ratings. Five of the divisions were related to the movement and armament of aircraft and were designated V-1 to V-5 ('V' being the US Navy symbol for aircraft). These divisions were under the control of the ship's air officer, who had command of the ship's aircraft when they were aboard the ship. They were:[6]

V-1 – In charge of aircraft movement on the flight deck, including deciding where and when to spot aircraft on the deck. Its complement of nine officers and two warrant officers included the LSOs, the arrester gear officers and the flight deck officers. Its duty stations were at Fly I and Fly II.[7] This was the division, along with the next, to which the 'airdales' (aviation bosuns' mates) were generally assigned.

V-2 – In charge of aircraft handling on the hangar deck. Its duty station was hangar control.

V-3 – In charge of the arrester gear and catapults, keeping them in working order. When not so involved, they served as a repair crew. The division officer's duty station was secondary air control.

V-4 – In charge of aviation ordnance, including the movement of such ordnance on deck and the actual rearming of aircraft. Its duty station was Fly III, aft on the flight deck.

V-5 – A small division in charge of such diverse support activities as weather reporting and predicting, air plotting and air intelligence. It had a number of duty stations, including weather plot, air plot and radar plot.

The ship's divisions as opposed to the 'V' divisions were the XO's concern, although he delegated that responsibility to his various specialist officers, who, acting through their division officers, would have direct control of the relevant divisions. Thus, the first lieutenant had responsibility for divisions 1, 7, 12 and 13, because they were responsible for damage control. The gunnery officer had control of divisions 2 to 6, because those divisions manned the ship's guns in combat and kept them in repair. The communications officer controlled divisions 8, 9 and 10. Division 11 was the responsibility of the ship's senior engineer, 14 of the senior supply officer and 15 of the senior medical officer. The responsibilities and/or duty stations of the ship's divisions were as follows:

1. This division was in charge of the exterior of the ship, its appearance and repair. This was the division to which most bosun's mates were assigned. Its combat duties involved 5in guns, their repair, direction and manning.
2. Sky Forward look-outs and the manning of various 5in, 40mm and 20mm guns.
3. Manning various 40mm mountings.
4. Sky Aft look-outs and the manning of various 5in and 40mm mountings.
5. Manning various 40mm and 20mm guns. This division was composed of the ship's Marines.
6. 5in gun direction and aft ammunition handling.
7. Based at Central Station, this division manned Repair II and Repair III and had specific responsibility for gasoline (petrol) clean-up.
8. Responsible for the ship's radios.
9. Manned Battle II, the auxiliary control station at the aft end of the funnel.
10. Responsible for the ship's IC systems.

Above left: The crew seldom gathered on deck, so it is often hard to get an idea of the number of men who inhabited the 'Lexingtons'. One of the rare occasions that brought the men together was PT (Physical Training), in this case calisthenics in the sun on *Saratoga*'s flight deck, in some South Pacific harbour, October 1943. (NARA)

Above: The crew was divided into 20 divisions according to their combat assignments. Some divisions felt considerable pride in the accomplishment of their duties, exemplified by this sign over the door to *Saratoga*'s V-4 office in the funnel structure aft on the flight deck, February 1944. The insignia is that of an aviation ordnanceman, wings on a grenade. The lettering across the bottom reads: 'Through this door walk the men who keep 'em firing'. (NARA)

Above: The men of V-4 were also distinguished by the colour of their caps, yellow with a red stripe. Here V-4 ordnancemen on *Saratoga* haul 100lb bombs from the bomb lift (upper left) to a stack on the flight deck where fuses were inserted and the bombs made ready to hang under the wings of Hellcats, November 1943. (NARA)

Above right: Many treatments of the US Navy in the Second World War ignore the presence of minorities on ships. A small number of Blacks and Filipinos were part of the crew, mainly as mess attendants. The Navy, indeed the US military in general, would not de-segregate until after the war. Here three of *Saratoga's* small crew of messmen (there were 38 of them in 1938) relax in a 40mm guntub, March 1944. Note the empty racks for ready-use ammunition along the inner face of the guntub. (NARA)

11. Engineering staff, based at Main Control, responsible for power systems.
12. Manned Repair V.
13. Manned Repair IV.
14. Responsible for coding and decoding messages. This division was composed of the ship's supply officers.
15. Medical and dental personnel, manned the dressing stations and sick bay.

The crew stood watches on a regular rotation. The day was divided into six four-hour watches. From midnight, these were: Mid, Morning, Forenoon, Afternoon, Dog and Evening. The only one of these that was unusual in any way was the Dog watch, which was split into two two-hour half watches (First Dog and Second Dog), so that the crew then on watch could eat dinner in rotation. The basic watch rotation for all hands, with few exceptions, was four hours on and four hours off. The main exception was the look-outs, who stood two-hour watches, since fatigue limited the time that a look-out could be effective. There were enough look-outs on station for the actual duty time of any one man to be even less than two hours.[8] Unlike regular wartime practice in the Royal Navy, the US Navy did not stagger watch rotations:

'I think probably on a small ship that would be more in order than on the *Saratoga*. She's so big and spread out that your change of watches happens through about a half an hour anyway.'[9]

The regular watch schedule was always subject

to interruption by the demands of combat. There were three regular readiness conditions and two combat conditions which affected the manner in which watches were stood. The regular conditions were numbered One to Three in order of decreasing readiness.[10] The combat conditions were Flight Quarters, in which all aircraft handlers and squadron personnel were at their ready stations in preparation for immediate flying operations, and General Quarters (GQ), in which all ship's personnel were at battle stations. The combat conditions were expected to be temporary, in that, at GQ, most regular ship activities came to a halt. The regular conditions were designed for extended duration, depending on the perceived level of threat of combat. The condition chosen had a direct impact on the length of time it took to get to GQ, and was chosen with that factor in mind, as well as the impact of higher readiness over extended periods on crew fatigue. The decision as to the readiness state was a trade-off between reaction time and crew condition:

'At first we started standing Condition Three at night. I don't think it's adequate. It takes too long to get the crews to their battle stations from Three. With Two you've got a skeleton - the Two is a little different now than the Two we used to think of where we had half our battery manned. We think it's preferable now to put half the gun crews on all the guns, with enough ammunition up to keep 'em going until the crew can get to general quarters. So that every gun has enough people there to open fire in Condition Two.'[11]

On average, it took about 10 to 12 minutes to

get to GQ from Condition Two.[12] When *Saratoga* was hit by Kamikazes off Iwo Jima in February 1945, the order to commence firing came just 10 minutes after GQ was sounded and not all batteries were fully manned.[13] Generally GQ was maintained only when there was an actual threat present. The exception to this was at dawn and dusk, which traditionally are the times of greatest vulnerability to enemy attack:

> 'You go to general quarters – different Admirals have different times – some would say a half hour before sunrise, some an hour before sunrise. You remain at quarters, usually just a little after sunrise. In the evening, you go a half-hour to an hour before sunset and stay until maybe a half-hour after twilight ends. During those times at general quarters you enliven them by having all kinds of departmental drills.'[14]

Appearance of the Crew

At sea, the crew wore work clothes almost all the time, the officers in khaki and the men in a chambray work shirt and denim dungarees.[15] Headgear was almost always optional; in the work uniform, the crew wore the traditional upturned sailor's cap in white or navy blue, while officers wore a khaki fore-and-aft cap or a khaki version of the peaked dress cap. A baseball-style billed cap was also common working gear for officers. A black tie was available for the officer's khaki uniform but was rarely worn except at dinner. For the purposes of uniform, CPOs and warrant officers dressed in the same manner as commissioned officers. For cooler weather, officers had a khaki cotton windbreaker; the crew a similar garment in navy blue. Very cold weather, such as was common in the North Atlantic, required a thick navy blue sweater or pea coat, but this was rarely encountered by the 'Lexingtons', which spent most of their time in the relatively warm climate of the Central and South Pacific. In wet weather, there were rubberized slickers, hooded or with separate sou'wester cap. Whites were worn only in port or on ceremonial occasions. The crew was given considerable freedom in customizing their work dress. Depending on the weather, they would be found in work shirt, either full-sleeve or artificially short-sleeved, in tee shirt or singlet or even bare-chested.

Battle dress added a kapok life jacket and steel helmet to the work uniform. Any aviators, even ones not in flying billets, wore a 'Mae West' inflatable life vest in place of the kapok jacket.

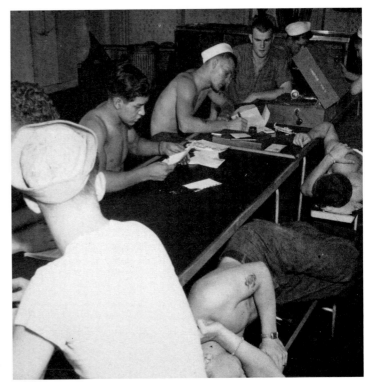

Left: Standard work uniform for officers and men, worn 99 per cent of the time, is shown in this view of payday on *Saratoga*, February 1944. The warrant officer on the right, in charge of the cashbox, wears the typical khaki shirt and peaked cap. The enlisted crewmen in line to get paid wear the light blue chambray work shirt and dark blue denim dungarees. (NARA)

The crewmen of the aviation divisions wore singlets and helmets in distinctive colours so that their officers and mates could instantly identify the role they were playing on deck. Members of these divisions were sometimes further identified by a large stencilled number on their shirt and/or a stripe on their helmet. For example, a blue shirt identified an aircraft handler, responsible specifically for the chocks and chains used to secure aircraft on deck. Blue shirts could be recruited for any other aircraft handling duty, as needed. A yellow shirt identified a taximan, or plane director; these crewman guided the movement of aircraft around the deck. A yellow helmet with a red stripe identified a V-4 ordnanceman.

Berthing the Crew

The crew of the 'Lexingtons' lived in specified areas of the ship based on rank or rate. The berthing arrangements for each group were as follows:

Wardroom Officers – berthed mainly forward on the main deck, although a small number were housed on the upper half deck in the large space between junior officers' country and the wardroom. The cabins on the main deck were assigned by rank or position. The captain's cabin, with its associated stateroom

and pantry, dominated the starboard side of wardroom officers' country. The admiral had similarly sized accommodation off to the port side.[16] The admiral had a guest cabin just aft of his own and six cabins for his staff. The executive officer's cabin and stateroom were located just aft of the captain's cabin, on the starboard side. Other officers with specifically assigned cabins included the CAG and his squadron COs, the medical, supply, ordnance, engineering and electrical officers and the navigator, the first lieutenant and the senior marine officer.

Junior Officers – berthed forward on the upper half deck in cabins accommodating one or two men.

Warrant Officers – berthed forward on the middle half deck in one-man cabins.

CPOs – berthed forward on the third deck. They were housed in large open compartments on pipe berths constructed of welded metal tubing supporting a mattress.

POs – were berthed in many locations throughout the ship, wherever there was space to install some pipe berths. They were concentrated in the narrow compartments that ran along the side of the hangar on the second deck and the middle and upper half decks. They also berthed in the storerooms and shops

Left: Enlisted crewmen relax in one of their living compartments in *Saratoga*, 16 November 1944. The living quarters on the main deck had poor ventilation and were often hot, explaining the general state of undress. These tables were used for eating and, as here, for miscellaneous activities during the day. At night they were stowed out of the way and hammocks were slung from the overhead. (NARA)

Right: An epidemic of tonsillitis broke out in *Lexington* in March 1938, leading to an inspection of all crewmen for signs of the infection. Note the variety in work dress of the crewmen lined up for the doctor. (NARA)

Left: One of the rare occasions when the crew dressed in their whites was for the quarterly review and inspection. This one is taking place on *Lexington*, 18 March 1930. *Saratoga*, anchored in the background, is probably undergoing the same ordeal. (NARA)

Below left: This corpsman on *Saratoga* wears the navy blue windbreaker, a popular garment in chilly weather, November 1943. Officers had a similar garment in khaki. Note the special cap, marked with a red cross indicating his status as a medic, worn under the helmet. (NARA)

Below: *Saratoga*'s Fly I officer in November 1943 was Lieutenant J. Briscoe. His tee shirt with rolled up sleeves and cap were typical flight deck fashion in hot weather. (NARA)

Above: Fliers were officers but had a style all their own. They wore the standard officer's work uniform of khaki shirt and trousers, but when on the job they added a yellow 'Mae West' life-jacket and a leather flying cap with integral headphones and throat mike. (NARA)

Above: In an obviously posed picture aboard *Saratoga* in November 1943, the flight deck officer, an assistant and a talker man their position in bad weather gear while the CO, Captain J.H. Cassady, looks over the screen separating the new Pri-Fly from the rest of the navigation bridge. (NARA)

Right: All bets were off when King Neptune ruled. When a ship crossed the equator, 'polliwogs', meaning any who had not crossed the line, were subject to harassment by the 'shellbacks' who had, regardless of rank. The 'polliwogs' were covered with a foul-smelling mixture and had to run a gauntlet between rows of 'shellbacks' wielding canvas flails. This ritual is seen on *Lexington*, 20 May 1936. (NARA)

Left: Seamen, any enlisted crewman below the rank of petty officer, slept in a hammock on the 'Lexingtons'. Washing hammocks was a regular ritual involving a broom and salt water soap, *Lexington*, 7 May 1928. (NARA)

Left: After the hammocks were washed and rinsed, they were hung up from the signal yards. Note the 6pdr saluting guns forward of the funnel, *Lexington*, 24 May 1928. (NARA)

aft of the hangar on these decks. These berths, stacked three or four high, folded up when not in use.[17]

Seamen were berthed in large compartments dominating the aft sections of the main deck.

'Non-rated men slept in hammocks on the mess deck. They were very comfortable in any type of sea, once a person learned to get into them. We started with hammocks in boot camp and kept them. I still have mine. Hammocks were hung high enough so that, by a little bending of the neck, they could be walked under. Doors from the mess compartment were wide open so we got plenty of fresh air. When reveille sounded the MAA (Master at Arms) crew came through shouting. If not out

of the hammock on their return trip you got whacked with a club, right where the hammock sagged the most, or the edge of the hammock was grasped by one edge and you were flipped out onto the deck, bedding and all. When properly packed, lashed and stowed the hammock and seabag could also be used as a one-man life raft.[18]

Marines – were berthed in a separate area of the main deck surrounding the forward elevator.

Mess Attendants – were berthed in their own separate area adjacent to the Marines' spaces and near the crew's galley spaces in the middle of the main deck.

The neat arrangements just described worked only as long as the ships were at or under designed complement. Wartime brought vastly increased crew size with the concomitant demands for berthing space. Already in early 1942, the situation was straining the ships' ability to find room for the added crew:

'The battery personnel is growing tremendously. We added 140 people to take care of the guns alone in the deck divisions, and of course there had to be the following additional overhead, galley personnel, storekeepers - and I don't know where the ships are going to stop. We ripped out some of the staterooms and put in a lot of standee-bunks for officers, and still had to resort to putting cots in the passageways. But those things seem to be necessary under the circumstances. So, you're in a constant turmoil as to where to sleep your people.'[19]

Ventilation of the living and working spaces within the hull remained a constant problem. Even when the ships were new and relatively uncrowded, the ventilation was meagre at best:

'The air grew quite foul at times, there being no air-conditioning. Airlines and vents were designed to furnish a change of air but it was either a cold blast or no air at all. Metal airscoops were put in opened ports in calm weather to gather in more air, especially in tropical waters. They had to be watched however, because if given a chance they also gathered in goodly portions of the waves.'[20]

The ventilation problem was actually worse in the wardroom officer's country on the main deck. In particular, there existed an

'...excess of artificial supply over artificial exhaust to and from the lower decks...foul and heated air necessarily rises through companion ways and hatches up to the level of the main deck. Where this ascending column of air meets the underside of the flight deck there are no openings in this deck through which it can escape. This contaminated air must therefore seek the easiest way out to the surrounding atmosphere and this path is through the Admiral's, Captain's and officers' staterooms and country. These living spaces become foul and overheated, particularly the inboard rooms.'[21]

Obviously, this situation was intolerable, particularly since the location with the worst problem was immediately outside the admiral's cabin. Exhaust fans were fitted in an attempt to relieve the problem, with better success in *Lexington* than in *Saratoga*. The ultimate losers in this rearrangement were the poor souls who lived or worked in the lower sections of the ships:

'A defect in the installation of these fans is that the discharge outlets in several instances are immediately adjacent to the supply inlets of the original fans which furnish air to the lower decks. This results in a direct short-circuit, and the pumping of hot vitiated air back into the spaces below.'[22]

Despite all attempts to alleviate the tremendous accumulation of heat in the lower decks, particular in the tropics, the problem proved basically insoluble. The crew that worked in the lower decks just learned to tolerate extremes of heat. In *Lexington*'s engine room the heat often reached 120°F during the day, dropping a few degrees at night.[23] As late as 1943 *Saratoga* reported that temperatures averaged 100°F in main control and reached 120°F in the after distribution room with one motor generator running and 130°F if both were running.[24]

1. GenBd, GenBd -> SecNav, 3 May 1922, Building Programme 1922 - Battle Cruisers 1 - 6 Class converted to Airplane Carriers. These figures were obviously preliminary but give a good idea of the size of crew originally intended. The figures listed in this section do not include squadron personnel, who were always counted separately.
2. I&S, 4 November 1931, Report of Material Inspection of U.S.S. *Lexington* (CV2), p 4-5.
3. I&S, 1 July 1938, U.S.S. *Saratoga* (CV3) - Material Inspection of, p II -1-2.

Below: Petty officers merited pipe-berths and a thin mattress in the place of hammocks. A hot card game is going on in this berthing space, *Saratoga*, November 1943. The pipeberths were suspended four deep from the deckhead; when not in use, they were stowed, leaving the space available for other uses. (NARA)

4. BuShips, 1 December 1942, U.S.S. *Saratoga* - Roster of Officers.

5. I&S, 1 July 1938, U.S.S. *Saratoga* (CV3) - Material Inspection of, p II - 2.

6. Powers, Bill, If We're Not Here - They Don't Go, in The Hook, Spring 1982, p 10-16.

7. The flight deck was split in thirds for purposes of spotting aircraft and controlling the movement of deck crewmen. From the bow aft, they were Fly I, II and III.

8. Each look-out had responsibility for a 60° arc of the horizon or sky, meaning that six battle look-outs and six sky look-outs, in theory, were all that were required. Nevertheless, *Saratoga* always had sixteen look-outs of each type on duty at any one time, so they could spell each other regularly.

9. ibid, p 8.

10. Condition One means full readiness; Condition One for the entire ship's company is the same as GQ. The only reason why Condition One exists as a separate state is because it is possible to set Condition One for one ship's department and a different condition for others.

11. op. cit., p 10.

12. ibid, p 3. Motivation had much to do with the time it took to get to GQ. After her first torpedoing, according to Pride, it took only eight minutes to get to GQ from Condition Two.

13. BuShips, Sara -> CinCUS, 26 February 1945, U.S.S. *Saratoga* (CV3) Action Report for period 0900 (K) to 2130 (K), 21 February 1945 - forwarding of, p 10.

14. op. cit., p 9.

15. ibid, p 10. The uniform changed very little during the life of the 'Lexingtons', except that the crew's dress flat cap was supplanted by the upturned sailor's cap and the navy blue work jumper, a blue version of the white dress jumper, was replaced by the chambray work shirt.

16. By naval tradition inherited from the Royal Navy, a ship's captain and the admiral (if the ship was a flagship) kept separate tables, hence their separate pantries.

17. Leslie, Max R., Lady Lex - The Early Days, in The Hook, Fall 1981, p 13.

18. ibid.

19. BuShips, , 16 June 1942, Interview of Commander Alfred M. Pride, USN, in the Bureau of Aeronautics, p 7.

20. The Hook, Fall 1981, p 13.

21. I&S, , 4 November 1931, Report of Material Inspection of U.S.S. *Lexington* (CV2), p 60-1.

22. ibid.

23. Queen, p 7.

24. BuShips, Sara -> BuShips, 6 October 1943, U.S.S. *Saratoga* (CV3) - Alteration Request No. 27-43 (Ventilation System).

2.4 Provisions

Feeding the Crew

Foodstuffs were stored in the 'Lexingtons' in storerooms on the first platform deck, one for each mess, and refrigerated spaces on the third deck. These included separate lockers for the crew's meat and butter and eggs and smaller refrigerators specific to the other messes. The dry provision storeroom capacity was sufficient for 180 days; cold storage capacity was considered sufficient for 45 days.[1] A later inspection of *Saratoga* gave the dry storage

capacity as 181 days' worth, or 363.35 tons, but the cold storage as only 32 days.[2]

The butcher's shop, bakery, potato peeling room and the main scullery were all located in the middle section of the main deck, adjacent to the large crew's galley and the smaller officer's galley, where most of the cooking for the ship was done. The crew's galley was dominated by eight huge steam kettles and two large roasting ovens.[3] The crew had no separate mess area, each crew berthing space doubling as an eating space (and lounge area as well). Officers' food, having been cooked in the officers' galley, was prepared for serving in the pantry associated with the individual mess. The CPOs' mess area and pantry were located forward on the second deck. The warrant officers and junior officers had separate mess and pantry areas on the middle half deck. The wardroom and its associated pantry were located forward on the upper half deck. The admiral's and captain's pantries were near their cabins on the main deck; they dined in their cabins unless invited to the wardroom by the ship's senior officers. There was also a small diet kitchen located forward on the second deck adjacent to the sick bay.

In the 'Lexingtons'' early days, the entire crew was fed at set times:

'We lined up for chow on the 5in AA platform and the flight deck above the

Above: Officers had permanent berths in dedicated staterooms. Senior officers, such as *Saratoga*'s navigator in February 1944, Commander Beebe, got single accommodations with a porthole. (NARA)

Above: Admiral Somerville, Royal Navy, inspects *Saratoga*'s galley during a courtesy visit at the end of two months of joint operations in the Indian Ocean between TG58.5 (*Saratoga* and three USN destroyers) and the RN Eastern Fleet, 16 May 1944. The cooks are dressed in traditional white. Note the massive kettle on the left. *Saratoga*'s crew's galley had eight such kettles. (NARA)

Above right: Senior officers messed in the wardroom. Officers were expected to dress for dinner, which during wartime meant wearing a black tie with the khaki work uniform, especially when there were distinguished guests, such as Admiral Nimitz, who attended *Saratoga*'s 17th birthday party on 16 November 1944. Filipino and Black messboys, wearing ties, carried food to the tables; mess attendants, three of whom wait their turn in the background, bussed the tables. (NARA)

platform. When piped down, a mad rush was made for the tables. The old timers, married men and rated lived ashore when we were based on North Island and had commuted rations. Aboard ship some of them grabbed the end spot at the tables and grabbed the food containers as soon as the messcook stepped over the coaming of our compartment.'[4]

This system worked well until war came and it became impractical to set up specific mealtimes for the entire crew:

'Of course, you have to feed right around the clock now, with half your crew on watch all night you just keep your galley and your messes set up all the time. We installed a complete cafeteria system in the *Saratoga* in the yard and that fixed that. They run all night cafeteria and people come in and eat when they want to and it works out.'[5]

The same system was tried out very briefly in the wardroom. The experiment lasted only a week before the senior officers forced a return to a more conventional schedule.[6]

As built, the 'Lexingtons' had no gedunk (Soda Fountain).[7] This oversight was resolved before war broke out and a full-service soda fountain was in operation on the 'Lexingtons' serving ice cream sundaes and sodas in all their varieties. This was critical since the US Navy

allowed no alcohol aboard ship; ice cream was every bit as important to the US sailor as grog was in the Royal Navy.

Liquids

Water
Water was piped throughout the ship to provide for drinking, cooking and sanitary requirements. Fresh water always seemed to be in short supply in the early days:

'We were issued galvanized buckets and about twice a day fresh water was turned on. We drew fresh water under the gaze of a member of the Master at Arms force, heated it under a steam jet and then were free to use it for anything we cared, wash shave, brush our teeth, scrub clothes, just don't dare waste it. A bath could be taken in salt water, using a salt water soap, but it was not very satisfactory, always a little sticky feeling.'[8]

All fresh water on board was distilled from sea water, not just that made available to the crew for drinking or sanitation, but also the feed water used in the ships' boilers to drive the turbines. Distillation was done by two sets of evaporators which could produce about 250 tons of water in a 24-hour period. This just covered the requirements of the boilers which,

71

Above: On normal days the OOD sampled the crew's food. This was a traditional act, a formality, since the 'chow' was uniformly good. Here, he sits in a food storage room sampling the chow on 5 November 1943. Note the walls lined with institutional-size tins of various foodstuffs, including jell-o. (NARA)

Above: Aircrew expected food after returning from a long mission so the squadron ready rooms were stocked with sandwiches and fruit for the returning fliers, *Saratoga*, November 1943. Fresh fruit at sea would have been impossible before the advent of refrigerated food storage. (NARA)

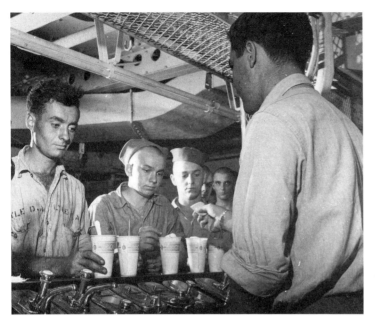

Above: The 'gedunk' was an institution in US Navy ships; the ice cream soda was as important to the US Navy as grog was to the Royal Navy. The gedunk was in fact a full-service soda fountain and ice cream could be had in many different ways. Generally, crew members paid a nominal amount for their ice cream, the money going to the crew's recreational fund, which paid for, among other things, the beer available to the crew on shore liberty. (NARA)

Left: The crew's mess spaces doubled as sleeping areas. The mess tables were hauled up to the deckhead, as the one at the top, and hammocks were slung from the rows of hooks running down the centre of the compartment, *Saratoga*, 2 September 1942. (NARA)

in the same 24-hour period, consumed 235 tons when steaming at high speed. Given a fresh water requirement of 15 gallons per day per man for drinking, washing and cooking, the ships' complements would consume 112 tons per day, leaving an obvious shortfall.[9]

Drinking water was piped into a pair of holding tanks underneath the saluting gun platform at the forward end of the funnel and from there to scuttlebutts located throughout the ship. The water in these fountains was cooled by brine piped from the ice machines. This system was replaced in *Lexington* in 1941 by a set of nineteen electric water-coolers. These were standard civilian units designed to cool the water at the unit by means of a small electric compressor-driven refrigeration unit. They worked well in the yard at Bremerton, when the ambient air temperature averaged 70°F, but proved less than satisfactory in Hawaiian waters, where the ambient temperatures ran 15°F higher.[10]

Oil

At the time of her construction, *Lexington* had a fuel oil capacity of 1,592,000 gallons under normal loading; in an emergency, this figure could be increased by approximately 300,000 gallons, but only by accepting a starboard list until the extra fuel oil was burned off.[11] Not all this oil was readily available due to the high viscosity of naval bunker fuel and the location of the suction heads in each tank. In 1931 it was estimated that 116,000 gallons out of the above

total was unrecoverable by normal means.[12] Oil was always the limiting factor in ship operations:

> 'Those who have been on the *Lexington* and *Saratoga* will recollect that for years we comforted ourselves with the thought that if we were in a jam, we could always draw on the fuel oil that was used to balance the starboard structure, that 360,000 gallons of fuel oil that had been carried since the day the ship was commissioned. Well, we found much to our dismay that running at 21 knots, which is the speed you like because you don't feel that a submarine can overhaul you very well – at that speed, your oil gang just can't drain down the tank as fast as the oil is being used. They'll get a tank down two-thirds and jump to another tank to avoid the chance of losing suction. So you'll get down to about 400,000 gallons and find your fires going out. We did that. We ran out of oil making the dock at Pearl Harbor on one occasion – our fires went out just as I'd got the lines out. We'd come in through the channel on the oil from our diesel tanks and when we sounded our tanks afterwards we had 400,000 gallons of fuel oil still in the ship; and the ship was dead in the water.'[13]

One method of overcoming this limitation on range imposed by fuel capacity was the new idea of underway replenishment (UNREP). This is now a common method of resupply, allowing aircraft-carrier groups to operate more or less indefinitely on station, but between the wars it was still experimental. The method originated with the idea of using the large fuel capacity of the 'Lexingtons' as a means of resupply for short-ranged escorts, particularly destroyers. Already, in 1931, *Lexington*'s inspection board recommended that the apparatus be installed that would allow the 'broadside oiling' of destroyers while under way.[13] This was apparently done, because a letter of 30 July 1935 from ComAirBatFor indicates that the 'Lexingtons' were capable of refuelling one destroyer on each side and of delivering fuel at an aggregate rate of 140,000 gallons an hour.[15]

The idea of reversing the process, of refuelling the 'Lexingtons' from an oiler, originated somewhat later, but was at least at the experimental stage in 1935. In the same letter, ComAirBatFor complained that it took far too long to fill the 'Lexingtons'' bunkers, but that the problem lay not with the carriers but with the inadequate pumping capacity of the Navy's existing oilers.[16] A report of an UNREP exercise involving *Saratoga* and the oiler *Kanawha* (AO-1) held in 1939 reported complete success. The technique had by now been perfected to the

Left: The underway replenishment (UNREP) of escorts was common practice by the time this photo of *Humphreys* (DD236) was taken from *Lexington* in May 1934. (NARA)

point that the greatest concerns were the best approach angles, the best towing technique and the correct hose size.[17] The critical point is that UNREP had now become commonplace to the point that fine details were all that remained to be resolved. The technique would be available for use throughout the war.

Gasoline

Saratoga carried 140,000 gallons of gasoline (petrol) for use as aviation fuel.[18] Despite the far smaller quantity, compared with fuel oil, many more precautions had to be exercised in the storage and transfer of avgas, because of the different volatility of the two fuels. Bunker oil is thick and tends not to evaporate in a closed tank; if touched by flame, it burns. Avgas is highly volatile and will fill up any free tank

space with gasoline fumes, a vapour of gasoline and air. This is a highly explosive mixture and if touched by flame in an enclosed space will explode like a bomb.

The avgas tanks, though far fewer in number than the oil tanks, presented a far greater danger, and considerable effort was expended in an attempt to find the safest location. The best that could be found was forward, on both sides, between Frames 44 and 75, where the number of tanks forming a protective layer between the hold and the third deck was increased from four tanks to five and, for a short span, six. Seven tanks on each side were used for the storage of avgas. There was always a void, a water-filled tank or an oil tank between the gasoline and the shell plating on the outside or the working spaces on the inside of the ship. As experience

with *Lexington* would show, this was insufficient to provide safety.[19]

To minimize the danger of explosion in the avgas system – both in the tanks themselves and the pipes that carried the fuel up to the aircraft on the flight deck – a way had to be found to displace any free air in the system. As built, the 'Lexingtons' were provided with a water replacement system that filled any air space in the avgas tanks with a similar volume of water. This proved satisfactory as far as it went, but it did not protect the piping and surrounding void spaces, which would certainly contain avgas vapour even if the tanks were topped up with liquid. As early as June 1939, it was suggested that an inert gas system be installed in the 'Lexingtons', although this had been done to neither ship prior to the outbreak of war.[20]

On *Lexington* up to the time of her loss, the practice had been to fill the void tanks around the avgas tanks with water to prevent an accumulation of vapour. However, this seemingly prudent practice seems to have contributed to her loss (see Chapter 5). *Saratoga* was fitted with an inert gas system during her first wartime refit:

> 'I'm told that with the *Lexington* there was water in the voids around the gasoline tanks right up to the gasoline. Now, the *Saratoga* has those voids void except for inert gas. During the last time in the yard we had a little internal combustion engine installed up beneath the old torpedo workshop and the only thing in the world that engine does is run an exhaust into those voids around the gasoline tanks.'[21]

The idea behind the inert gas system was simplicity itself. The exhaust from a gasoline-powered internal combustion engine running on a very lean fuel mixture would be very high in CO_2 content and, if the mixture was tuned properly, low in dangerous CO. Carbon dioxide, being denser than air, will tend to settle at the lowest points, displacing any air in the same space. By displacing any free air, the CO_2 prevents any combustion (or explosion) from taking place; by forming a dense 'blanket' over any free surface of gasoline, it tends to reduce the tendency of the gasoline to vaporize.[22] The system was virtually self-contained since it ran on the very gasoline it was intended to protect and it drove its own compressor to provide the pressure necessary to force the exhaust into void tanks.

The only complaint *Saratoga* had after using the inert gas system for a year was that it had to be run continuously in order to provide enough exhaust. That was because it was being used not only to provide an inert 'filling' for the void spaces around the gasoline tanks, but also to flush avgas vapours out of the piping that ran from the tanks to the flight deck:

> 'It is the practice of this vessel, while operating in dangerous waters, to blow back with inert gas all fuelling lines and hoses after each fuelling operation. This operation requires approximately 350 cubic feet of inert gas, and it is necessary to blow back several times in one day's flight operations.'[23]

Since the plant's capacity was 500 cubic feet per hour, and since the void tanks needed regular recharging with inert gas, this capacity was seen as inadequate. *Saratoga* recommended a system with at least 50 per cent greater capacity. This change seems to have been made during the June-September 1944 refit.[24]

As originally designed, the 'Lexingtons' had piping leading from the avgas tanks up to both sides of the flight deck forward (in Fly I). This decision made sense since any leakage or spills of avgas would dissipate harmlessly in the open air and Fly I was the logical place to refuel and rearm aircraft (aircraft could be worked on there while leaving the flying-on area free in Fly III). Nevertheless, this proved too restrictive in practice, as experience showed that aircraft located elsewhere on the flight deck or even in the hangar might equally need refuelling, and the difficulty of shuffling fuelled aircraft aft or down an elevator so that room could be made to move other aircraft into Fly I proved to be a major headache.[25] Plans were discussed concerning the refuelling of aircraft in the hangar.[26] The capacity of the fans ventilating the hangar deck was increased in anticipation of this being done, but good sense prevailed in the end and the idea was dropped. The problem was addressed, however, by increasing the number of refuelling outlets on the flight deck, the new outlets being located further aft. At first, the new avgas lines were run along the edge of the flight deck, but after a disastrous fire in *Enterprise*, they were moved further down the outside of the hull:

'Another thing that's happened on *Saratoga* – after the *Enterprise* had her fire we became concerned about the gasoline lines that were over the gun galleries. So when we got to

Bremerton we got those moved down the outside of the ship and people said, "Well, you know they used to be down there and they had to take them off because of damage," and I said, "Yes, I know that, but we'll take the damage from tugboats rather than the chance of a fire on the gun gallery, such as the Enterprise had".'[27]

Munitions

The 'Lexingtons' required spaces and systems for storing and handling a wide variety of

Above: An aircraft-carrier at war expended munitions, particularly aerial bombs, at a prodigious rate. A munitions lighter, seen alongside *Saratoga* at Majuro in January 1944, carries a cargo of 1,000lb bombs and other munitions for the forthcoming Operation 'Flintlock', the invasion of the Marshall Islands. (NARA)

Left: V-4 ordnancemen on *Saratoga*, 16 May 1944, sit casually on 500lb HE bombs waiting for the order to carry them to waiting SBDs. Bombs too heavy to carry by hand (anything larger than 100lb) were moved on a small handtruck. (NARA)

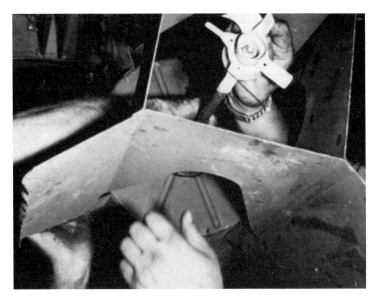

Above: Once the bomb was hung from the wing or bomb bay of the aircraft, the delicate operation of attaching the arming wire to the rack was performed by V-4 crewmen. Here, two crewmen wire up the tail fuse of an incendiary bomb on *Saratoga*, 31 July 1945. (NARA)
Below: Belts of .50cal ammunition are fed into the wing bays of an F6F Hellcat on *Saratoga*, 9 September 1945. (NA

munitions, including those required for the ships' own gun systems and those used by the aircraft in the carriers' air groups. (Details of the munitions themselves are given in Chapter 4; this section will describe where those munitions were stored and how they were moved to the sites where they were needed.)

Aviation Munitions

The magazines for aviation munitions were located mainly along the centre line of the ship, forward at the lowest levels. The only exception was aerial torpedoes, which were stored and maintained in a pair of compartments just forward of the forward elevator at upper half deck and main deck levels. The bomb elevator, which brought aerial bombs up from the magazines, was located well forward at Frame 58. It ran from the hold up to the third deck. There bombs were loaded onto trolleys and carted to a second bomb elevator just aft of the forward aircraft elevator machinery. This second elevator carried the bombs up one deck into the hangar; aircraft were originally to have been armed with bombs and torpedoes in the hangar and then raised, already armed, to the flight deck on one of the two aircraft elevators. Almost from the start this proved to be an unworkable arrangement. The aircraft elevators were too small and too slow (and too few) to permit aircraft to be stored in the hangar and brought to the deck only for launching. It became standard practice to store the air group on the flight deck and use the hangar only for maintenance. Consequently aircraft munitions had to be raised on one of the aircraft elevators up to the flight deck and the aircraft armed there. In 1931 *Lexington*'s inspectors found this method of arming aircraft to be unacceptable:

> 'The use of these elevators [lifts] means that a number of aircraft that would otherwise occupy the flight deck space in way of the elevators must be out of the way or else that bombs and torpedoes must be brought up in advance of the planes and kept in an exposed position on the flight deck, which is undesirable and dangerous. In addition, it is extremely difficult to transport the 1,000lb bombs and the torpedoes through the thickly massed planes on the flight deck. To conform with existing procedure of flight operations, it is therefore necessary to rearrange the torpedo and bomb stowage and handling facilities.'[28]

In fact, these changes were made quite early in *Lexington* and by the mid-1930s she had yet another bomb elevator installed just forward and to starboard of the forward aircraft elevator. Thus bombs were moved up from the magazines on the original pair of elevators, carted across the forward aircraft elevator in the hangar and then raised to the flight deck on the new elevator. This elevator ran through space formerly occupied by torpedo storage and the torpedo workshop. These were relocated to a mezzanine gallery deck on the starboard bulkhead of the hangar at upper half deck level and a torpedo elevator was installed from the mezzanine deck to the flight deck alongside No. 3 main battery mounting. These munitions changes in storage and handling had not been made in *Saratoga* by 1938, when it was included in the list of proposed modernizations developed by the General Board, but it had been accomplished by March 1940.[29]

The actual quantities of munitions stored for aircraft use varied considerably over the course of the 'Lexingtons'' careers, as aircraft, their munitions and their missions evolved. In May 1942 *Saratoga* was allowed the following aviation munitions:

100lb demolition bombs	700
325lb depth bombs	200
500lb demolition bombs	700
1,000lb demolition bombs	300
1,600lb armour-piercing bombs	54
AA bombs (types C and D)	1,350
100lb incendiary bombs	550

Translating this allowance into actual numbers of stowed bombs depended on the exact model of munition that was stored. For example, the actual stowage of 500lb demolition bombs was 574 Mk 12 Mod 1s or 789 Mk 12 Mod 2s, the difference in numbers being due to the fact that the former could safely be stacked only four high in the magazines while the latter could be stacked seven high.[30]

Gun Munitions

If anything, the means of moving munitions for the ships' guns was even more complex than those for aviation munitions. Magazines for the 5in AA guns were located fore and aft at the hold and second platform deck levels. 8in shells and powder were stored in separate magazines, fore and aft, on the first platform deck. A complex series of hoists and cross-deck conveyors brought these rounds from their respective magazines to the guns. The nature of the ships' layouts was such that the 1931 inspection board saw no solution to this over-complex system. In reference to the main batteries, the board said:

> 'The ammunition supply line to these mounts from magazines is exceedingly complicated and lengthy, requiring excessive manpower, mechanical appliances, and handling. Two series of widely separated vertical elevators with long connecting horizontal conveyors are installed. These objectionable features are inherent in the design of the vessel and are irremediable.'[31]

The problem was not eased by the replacement of the 8in main battery by 5in twin mountings and the rapid proliferation of light and medium AA guns after war broke out. For example, to get 5in rounds to the aft twin mountings (Nos. 3 and 4), it was necessary to load them on to a chain hoist in the 5in shell magazine and handling room on the second platform deck. This hoist carried the rounds up to the third deck, where they were transferred by hand a few feet to another set of chain hoists that carried them up to the main deck, near the port side of the ship. From there they were carried across to the starboard side on a conveyor belt and then transferred by hand to a longitudinal belt that carried them forward 20 frames and deposited them in a handling room at the base of No. 4 mounting.[32]

As with aviation munitions, the allowances for various munition types varied widely over the life of the ships. In March 1944, after the Hunters

Below: Ready-use rounds of 40mm ammunition were stored in cans, sixteen rounds (four four-round clips) per can, in ready-use lockers near the deck edge 40mm mountings. This rare view of a jumbled pile of 40mm cans shows the damage to a ready-use locker resulting from the Kamikaze attack on *Saratoga* on 21 February 1945. (NARA)

Point refit that saw the massive increase in 40mm guns at the expense of 20mm mountings, there was a major conversion of both 20mm and 5in magazines to hold 40mm rounds. The authorized levels of various rounds were 350rpg for each 5in/38 barrel and 1,800rpg for each 40mm barrel.[33]

1. I&S, 4 November 1931, Report of Material Inspection of U.S.S. *Lexington* (CV2), p 7.
2. I&S, 1 July 1938, U.S.S. *Saratoga* - Material inspection of, p II-3.
3. I&S, 5 September 1941, U.S.S. *Lexington* (CV2) - Material inspection of, p III-25.
4. The Hook, Fall 1981, p 14.
5. BuShips, , 16 June 1942, Interview of Commander Alfred M. Pride, USN, in the Bureau of Aeronautics, p 7.
6. ibid, p 8.
7. I&S, 4 November 1931, Report of Material Inspection of U.S.S. *Lexington* (CV2), p 52.
8. The Hook, Fall 1981, p 12.
9. op. cit., p 22. This document recommended an increase of 50 per cent in evaporator capacity.
10. BuShips, Lex -> BuShips, 25 November 1941, Drinking Fountains, automatic, electric.
11. op. cit., p 7. The 'Lexingtons' had a layer of three or more tanks around the outside of the ships below the third deck. The exact use of any tank could be changed by changing the piping to that tank, making exact figures for liquid capacities somewhat speculative.
12. ibid, p 7. In this case, 'normal means' means without resorting to the addition of sea water to the tank to float the oil up to the suction head.
13. BuShips, 16 June 1942, Interview of Commander Alfred M. Pride, USN, in the Bureau of Aeronautics, p3.
14. op. cit., p 80.
15. BuCon, ComAirBatFor -> BuCon, 30 July 1935, U.S.S. *Saratoga* (CV3) - Alteration Request No. 13-35 - Alteration to Fuel Oil Filling System - Request for - S55-1 (2nd Endorsement).
16. ibid.
17. BuShips, ComBaseFor -> CinCUS, 3 July 1939, *Saratoga* – *Kanawha* – Fuelling at Sea.
18. j24I&S, , 1 July 1938, U.S.S. *Saratoga* – Material Inspection of, p IX-2. The exact figure was 139,228 gallons, although, according to this report, *Saratoga* feared that this was inadequate for combat operations and wanted the capacity increased to 180,000 gallons. This had obviously not been done by mid-1942, because Commander Pride, in his 16 June 1942 BuAer interview said: 'Gasoline was never critical. It was always fuel oil that was critical. We had 140,000 gallons of gasoline aboard, and I never heard any question about running out of gasoline.'
19. At the Battle of the Coral Sea, *Lexington* was hit by a torpedo alongside her port avgas tanks, rupturing them and causing a slow leakage of gasoline fumes into the interior of the ship which, ignited by a spark in the IC room on the first platform deck, began the series of explosions that led to her loss.
20. BuCon, PSNY -> BuCon, 26 June 1939, U.S.S. *Saratoga* (CV3) - Gasoline System - Modernization.
21. BuShips, 16 June 1942, Interview of Commander Alfred M. Pride, USN, in the Bureau of Aeronautics, p 11.
22. BuShips, USS *New Orleans* -> CO Cruisers, Scouting Force, 10 February 1940, U.S.S. *Quincy* (CA39) - Gasoline System. This report was of the inert gas system installed experimentally in Quincy two years previously.
23. BuShips, Sara -> BuShips, 6 April 1943, U.S.S. *Saratoga* (CV3) – Inert Gas System, operation of. This document states that the system installed in *Saratoga* had originally been intended for the seaplane tender Albemarle (AV5).
24. BuShips, NYPS Departure Report.
25. As the 'Lexingtons' were modernized, the original bomb and torpedo elevators were moved to more central amidships locations (in Fly II) in response to the same problem.
26. I&S, 1 July 1938, U.S.S. *Saratoga* - Material Inspection of, p IX-1. It was recommended by the ship that the gasoline supply be altered to furnish outlets in the hangar spaces for refuelling planes prior to hoisting to the flight deck, and that sufficient ventilation be furnished, both supply blowers and exhaust outlets, to handle the fumes present during refuelling.
27. BuShips, 16 June 1942, Interview of Commander Alfred M. Pride, USN, in the Bureau of Aeronautics, p 11. The reference is to the fact that, as built, the 'Lexingtons' had their avgas piping outside the hull, but these were constantly being damaged by tugs and the like and so were moved inside the shell plating. Experience in the Second World War caused this piping to be moved outside again to prevent avgas leaks within the hull.
28. I&S, 4 November 1931, Report of Material Inspection of U.S.S. *Lexington* (CV2), p 29.
29. BuCon, PSNY -> BuCon, 26 March 1940, U.S.S. *Lexington* (CV2) and U.S.S. *Saratoga* (CV3) – Torpedo Stowage – Modernization, Groups II and VIII.
30. BuShips, NYPS -> BuShips, 15 May 1942, U.S.S. *Saratoga* (CV3) – Bomb Stowage – Forwarding Plans of.
31. I&S, 4 November 1931, Report of Material Inspection of U.S.S. *Lexington* (CV2), p 136.
32. BuShips, Sara -> BuShips, 14 April 1944, Hunters Point Departure Report. Obviously, little had changed from the handling of 8in rounds for the former main battery.
33. BuShips, Sara -> BuShips, 8 March 1944, USS *Saratoga* (CV3) - Alteration Request No. 11-43 and 12-43.

2.5 Sanitation

The analogy of a city and a fighting ship applies even to the less glamorous aspects of a city's services, in this case the sanitary systems. The 'Lexingtons' carried a population of well over 2,000 men into combat, men who had to keep clean and whose wastes had to be removed. As might be expected, these ships were a microcosm of the society that created them. This showed nowhere quite as clearly as in the size and location of the sanitary facilities and their assignment to the various groups of the crew. Since the US Navy was a military organization, the heads and washing facilities on board were segregated by rank. Given that American society at the time was racially segregated, it was not surprising that the only non-Caucasians on board, the Filipino and Black mess attendants, were provided with their own separate facilities.

Most of the sanitary facilities were located near the living quarters of the group to which they were assigned. Thus the CPOs' heads and showers were found forward on the second deck, the warrant officers' on the middle half deck, the junior officers' on the upper half deck and the wardroom officers' on the main deck. There was a small head on the upper half deck for wardroom officers berthed there adjacent to junior officers' country. (This one had originally been set aside for female guests but, due to complaints from wardroom officers berthed a deck below their fellows, the ladies' rest room was relocated on the middle half deck.[1]) The captain, admiral and his chief of staff each had a separate bath adjacent to their cabins. The crew's heads and showers were aft on the main deck. Crew members berthed elsewhere on the ship used these facilities as well. Those for the mess attendants were located on the main deck on the port side amidships. In addition, there were several other heads near work stations. A small head was provided on the second deck for the hangar crew and another was located on the port side of the main deck, accessible by gangway from the flight deck. There was a head on the middle half deck near the bank of ship's department offices for the use of the crew stationed there. A large washroom and head was located on the port side of the same deck for the use of the engineering crew.[2] There were three small heads in the island structure, one each at the flight deck, aerologic platform and navigation bridge levels. Two 'retiring rooms' were set aside for female guests, one on the middle half deck and one on the main deck.

The facilities were spartan, as might be expected on a warship. Nevertheless, the inspection board that examined *Lexington* in 1931 had a number of caustic comments to make about the equipment and layout of the ship's shower facilities.[3] The standard Navy shower piped steam into each individual shower head, heating the water there. This apparently made for a complex valve arrangement that was difficult to control and frequently inoperative. The inspectors also complained about the arrangement of the shower stalls which required the user to stand under the running water to adjust the water temperature. This arrangement, combined with the unpredictable nature of the shower head, led to frequent scaldings. The advent of war led to a number of problems that had been hidden by the more relaxed pace and lower crew levels of peacetime. The XO complained that it was hard keeping the men clean under combat conditions:

'They wear those damn kapok life jackets all day long and all night, and you just have to drive them to the showers...The dungarees get terribly dirty. The standard is there, but they're awfully hard to maintain...But you take these youngsters who'd probably had one, or possibly two, watches during the night – they're bound to get one during the day in Condition Three and they've got to have some time to clean themselves and eat – to say nothing of doing a little slacking off and resting. The result is that your ship suffers and you and the First Lieutenant just have to plug and plug.'[4]

By 1944 the crew's size in *Saratoga* had risen to the point that the captain was led to generate a ShipAlt requesting the modification of the crew's washrooms to accommodate the heavy congestion resulting from a significantly enlarged crew.[5]

1. I&S, 4 November 1931, Report of Material Inspection of U.S.S. *Lexington* (CV2), p 46. This change was recommended for *Lexington*; it had already been made on *Saratoga*.
2. op. cit., p 47. The 1931 inspection of *Lexington* found all the heads to be in good condition except for the firemen's. These were found to be very hot and subjected to very hard use. They recommended increased insulation and ventilation.
3. ibid, p 45-46.
4. BuShips, , 16 June 1942, Interview of Commander Alfred M. Pride, USN, in the Bureau of Aeronautics, p 9-10. Commander Pride was then the just relieved XO of *Saratoga*. He will be heard from again in this book.
5. BuShips, Sara -> BuShips, 10 June 1944, U.S.S. *Saratoga* (CV3) - Alteration Request No. 32-44 (Make minor alterations to the crews' washrooms).

Below: A shower in the officers' washroom on the main deck of *Saratoga*, February 1944. (NARA)

3. Protective Systems

3.1 Passive Protection

The passive protection systems built into the 'Lexingtons' fall basically into two categories: armour and watertight subdivision. The former is intended to prevent damage by slowing or stopping projectiles before they could pass into, and possibly explode inside, the ships' interior; watertight subdivision is designed to contain and control the spread of flooding or fire once it had begun. Thus armour is intended primarily to protect against gunfire and aerial bombs, which do their damage by impact and by internal explosion, while watertight subdivision is intended primarily to protect against torpedoes, which explode against the exterior of the hull and do their damage mainly by flooding.

Armour

The 'Lexingtons' started out as battlecruisers, a type of ship originally conceived by Jackie Fisher, best known as the creator of the dreadnought-type battleship. Fisher's real love, though, was the battlecruiser, which he conceived as the dreadnought version of an armoured cruiser. The battlecruiser was to carry the same calibre of gun as the dreadnought, although possibly fewer of them, at a significantly higher speed. Something had to be sacrificed to gain the speed advantage and that something was armour. The 'Lexingtons' were the US Navy's answer to the battlecruisers developed for the Royal Navy, from the 'Invincibles' to *Hood*. Like the RN's battlecruisers, the 'Lexingtons', when compared with the contemporary *South Dakota* (BB49) design, were to be faster (by approximately 11kt), more lightly armed (eight 16in guns vs. twelve 16in guns) and much more lightly armoured (8in belt vs. 14in). War experience with battlecruisers in the RN largely discredited the type, as no fewer than three were lost catastrophically during the Battle of Jutland in May 1916. Nevertheless, the RN began work on *Hood* after that battle, and the US Navy felt obliged to follow suit with its six 'Lexingtons'.

Right: A rare glimpse of *Saratoga*'s armoured belt, courtesy of a Japanese torpedo, seen off Tonga, 10 September 1942. The torpedo that hit the ship's starboard side in August 1942 caused forward repair crews to cut away the damaged sections of the broad stability bulge on that side, exposing the sloped armoured belt. (NARA)

When the Washington Treaty led to the decision to convert two of the 'Lexingtons' to aircraft-carriers, the armour scheme conceived for the battlecruisers was carried over largely intact, although its extent and thickness were generally reduced to save weight needed for aviation features. Where the battlecruisers were to have an armoured belt 16-17ft deep and 8in thick, the aircraft-carriers were to have a belt that was both less deep and less thick. The rule of thumb followed by BuOrd, which had cognizance over such matters, was that a ship's armour should be able to resist the gunfire of an equivalent ship. In general, that meant that the armour should be as thick as the calibre of the main battery weapon carried by the ship, although the calculation was complicated by such factors as expected range of engagement, angle of armour emplacement and whether the armour was external or positioned behind other bulkheads. Thus the 16in gunned 'South Dakotas' would have had an appropriate armoured belt (14in), while the similarly gunned 'Lexingtons', as battlecruisers, were consciously underarmoured (8in) to gain speed.

In order to define the correct armour layout and thickness for the redesigned 'Lexingtons', it was necessary to determine the opponents they would be likely to meet. The Navy's few airmen argued that armour, together with guns and most other traditional warship features, should be sacrificed to maximize aviation features, that aircraft-carriers would operate at a distance from any enemy surface ships and that aircraft were the only defence they needed. Advocates of the fast battleship wanted aircraft-carriers primarily for scouting, and envisaged the 'Lexingtons' being employed far out in front of the battle line, where they would be likely to encounter enemy scouting forces. That meant that the 'Lexingtons' needed appropriate armour to resist the gunfire of cruisers with 6in or 8in guns, which might well be encountered at night or in bad weather when, it was believed, aircraft could not operate.

Thus, in working up its plans for the new aircraft-carriers in May 1921, BuCon gave the planned carriers armour sufficient to resist 8in gunfire. This consisted of an armoured belt 12ft 6in high and 7in thick tapering downward to 4in. The belt was to be arranged vertically on the ship's side. The design waterline fell 6ft from the bottom of the belt. The armoured citadel was enclosed fore and aft by 7in thick transverse bulkheads. The upper surface of this armoured box was formed by a $2^3/4$-in protective deck, consisting of 2in of armour plate with a backing of 30lb STS, at third deck level. The armoured deck continued aft of the after transverse bulkhead, sloping gradually down over the steering compartments.

When BuCon had received no specific reaction from BuOrd to this armour layout by July 1921, it generated a memo listing three distinct options for the armour arrangement and asked BuOrd to choose one. These were: (A) a scheme identical to that proposed in May, with a flat armoured deck and vertical side armour; (B) a simple variant of (A) with a flat armoured deck, but with side armour inclined outwards as in the battlecruiser design; and (C) a new design which incorporated an inward sloping armoured deck, 5in thick, replacing the upper strake of the armoured belt.[1] Each of these schemes was compared in several factors: The effect of shells that failed to penetrate the armoured belt – scheme (A) wins because such shells simply fall overboard; scheme (B) deflects such a shell downwards with likely hull damage; with scheme (C) the shell is deflected upwards with potentially serious internal damage. Weight – scheme (B) is the heaviest and scheme (C) the lightest. Oil capacity – scheme (C) cuts into the planned oil capacity while the other two do not.

BuOrd expressed a strong preference for scheme (C) and it was this pattern that showed up in BuCon's revised design dated 9 September 1921. However, the decision to convert two battlecruisers instead of building the new aircraft-carriers from scratch meant that some variant of scheme (B) would be adopted, because that design was built into the already completed portions of the battlecruiser hulls. Another of BuOrd's preferences – mounting 8in guns on the converted 'Lexingtons' – led to the final revision of the armour scheme. To compensate for the increased weight of the main battery, it was decided to decrease the amount of armour still further.

The final design featured an armoured belt that was just 9ft $3^7/8$-in deep, the top 3ft being 7in thick, the rest tapering to 5in. This reduced height meant that the belt now ran only between the third deck and the first platform deck. The armoured deck was also reduced and was now a layer of 50lb STS over a backing of 30lb STS for a total thickness of 2in. This deck continued from the aft transverse bulkhead (at Frame 173) to the sternpost, but at a half deck lower level. A shallow transverse bulkhead of 60lb STS sealed the end of the armoured raft at Frame 201. The conning tower, located just below the navigation bridge, and the conning tower tube that ran down to the central station were both constructed of 80lb STS.

As early as the July 1921 memorandum, BuCon called attention to a potential problem with this scheme: the relatively shallow depth of the armoured belt and the fact that it extended only 6ft below the design waterline. When the ship was at high speed, the bureau feared that the trough behind the bow wave would expose the ship's side below the belt.[2] In fact, time was to show that the exact opposite was the problem; as the ships gained weight over their careers, particularly after the war began, the actual waterline rose well above the design waterline, increasingly submerging the belt.

By 1937 concern about the submergence of the armoured belt had reached the point that a search for remedies was begun. The first step was to calculate accurately the 'Lexingtons'' current displacement and draught and, from those figures, attempt to determine their likely displacement in battle condition. (Battle condition was defined as the state in which a ship would be when fighting a battle, namely with full crew, armament and munitions, but with only partial liquids and stores, since it was assumed that some percentage of these would be consumed getting there.) Thus, on 29 September 1937, *Saratoga* was found to have a mean draught of 30ft 11⅝-in, which represented a true displacement of 43,581 tons.[3] (Compare this figure with the planned 38,665 ton normal displacement to which they were designed.) BuCon then used this figure to calculate the probable battle displacement and the effect this had on the submergence of the armoured belt. The figures used for the variable weights were the maximum capacity of feed water, personnel, munitions, avgas and protective water in the tanks surrounding the avgas tanks. For provisions and general stores, two-thirds of

maximum capacity was allowed. Fuel oil was calculated as the maximum load possible with the ship on an even keel, 5,332 tons. *Lexington* now had an optimum battle displacement of 44,861 tons, leaving the top of her armoured belt 8⁷⁄₁₆-in above the waterline.[4]

The obvious problem with these calculations was that for the ships to reach some distant battle at optimum load, they would be leaving port in maximum or near maximum load condition. At the maximum stable load, *Saratoga*'s displacement was calculated as 48,044 tons, and at that displacement her armoured belt would be 1ft 2¹¹⁄₁₆-in below the waterline. *Lexington* was some 400 tons heavier and 2½-in lower in the water.[5]

Watertight Subdivision

The gradual raising of the waterline due to increased displacement meant much more than the submergence of the armoured belt. It meant that the whole basis on which the scheme of internal subdivision had been designed was no longer valid. That design had assumed that the waterline would remain well below the top of the armoured belt, which was, more significantly for this scheme, the level of the third deck. This deck, as well as being the armoured deck, was the upper limit of the area of the ship in which underwater damage was normally to be expected. It was the deck at which the upward movement of water within the hull was to be stopped. The entire scheme of watertight subdivision was neatly divided at the third deck. Below that deck, the system was designed to control the spread of water by a complex system of bulkheads, doors and scuttles. Above that level, the system was far looser, with watertight doors and bulkheads restricted to a few limited areas of the hull.

Below the third deck, the outer areas of the

Below: At Tonga, Navy divers did what they could to patch up *Saratoga* so she could sail back to Pearl Harbor for repairs. To aid their efforts, liquids were shifted inside the ship to give her a 9½ degree list to port, 9 September 1942. (NARA)

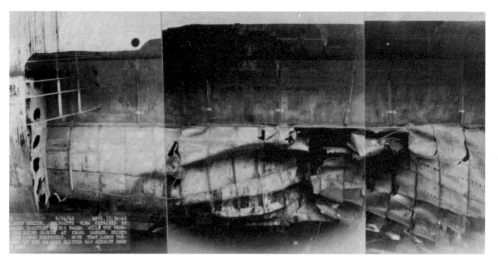

Left: Looking into the cutaway area of the starboard bulge shows the crushing of the outer layer of tanks, in the bulge below the armoured belt, the layer of emergency fuel oil tanks. This composite view was taken in the drydock at Pearl Harbor, 24 September 1942. (NARA)

hull were given over to layers of tanks and void spaces. These layers of tanks, like the layers of an onion, followed the curvature of the hull, each layer being divided from the next by internal bulkheads which ran continuously for most of the length of the ship. This system of layers of tanks on each side was connected across the bottom of the ship by a single layer of tanks known as the inner bottom. Along most of the length of the ship, this system of tanks was at least three layers deep, although the number of layers varied considerably, based both on the deck level and fore-aft location. At its narrowest, the system was only one or two layers wide at the bow, but for most of its length it was wider. For example, at the level of the second platform deck, the system began at Frame 25, was two layers wide to Frame 41, three wide to Frame 44, four wide to Frame 50, five wide to Frame 72, six wide briefly to Frame 74, five wide again for one frame and then four wide all along the side of the mechanical spaces to Frame 140, three wide to Frame 148 and then two wide until the last void tank ended at Frame 172. Its pattern at this level was for a thickness of four tanks to run most of the length of the ship, thinning fore and aft, except that a thick cluster of tanks was located just forward of the mechanical spaces in order to protect the avgas tanks.

Above the second platform deck, the system within the hull thinned by one layer because the shell plating curved inwards to meet the lower edge of the armoured belt. However, at this level, a new outer layer was provided by a narrow blister added over the shell plating and armoured belt in an attempt to add buoyancy and smooth the vertical line of the hull. As built,

this blister was symmetrical on both sides of the hull.

Most of the longitudinal bulkheads that made up this system were of 30lb STS. The innermost bulkhead was somewhat thicker, being 30lb STS over a base of 15lb STS. This bulkhead, known as the holding bulkhead, formed the inner wall of the primary defence against major flooding. All the tanks to the outside were small; if any void tank flooded, the effect on the ship's stability would be minor. Inside this bulkhead, however, were the capacious boiler and engine rooms. While each was a separate watertight compartment, they were of such size that the flooding of even one of these compartments would threaten the buoyancy and stability of the ship.

Above the third deck, the character and extent of the watertight subdivision changed completely. Alone among the longitudinal bulkheads, the holding bulkhead extended up to the middle half deck level, the intention being to prevent water from spreading along the length of the ship; it was assumed that water would only reach above the third deck when the ship was listing to one side and that the lateral spread of water beyond the holding bulkhead would be prevented by the slope of the deck. Above the second deck, almost no effort was made to compartmentize water. So many openings pierced the hull above this level and the hangar was such a large open space that any attempt to control the inflow or movement of water would have been futile. The only spaces given watertight integrity at this level were the boiler uptakes, to prevent water from pouring down and flooding otherwise intact compartments below the third deck.[6]

Above: While working up her air groups near Pearl Harbor for her role as a night carrier, *Saratoga* collided with a destroyer in her screen in late October 1944, sustaining minor damage. This view, taken in drydock at Pearl Harbor on 1 November 1944, shows temporary patches on her port side. Note the relatively small size of her port side bulge and the bilge keel below. (NARA)

Above right: The starboard bulge was wide enough to serve as a staging platform for transferring supplies from a lighter to the flight deck. This resupply operation took place at Trincomalee, 16 May 1944, at the end of *Saratoga*'s joint operations with the RN Eastern Fleet. (NARA)

The whole scheme of watertight compartmentation was of necessity pierced by innumerable hatches, scuttles and pipes. Crewmen had to move between compartments to do their jobs; tanks had to be inspected and cleaned. Similarly, pipes carrying liquids ran through compartments. Hatchways were closed by heavy watertight doors, scuttles by spring-loaded quick-closing covers. Pipes were provided with regularly spaced shut-off valves so that a rupture would not flood a compartment.

Just as there were readiness states that indicated the degree to which battle stations were manned, there were watertight conditions that indicated the degree to which these watertight doors, scuttles and valves were open or shut. On the 'Lexingtons' there were three of these conditions, known as X, Y and Z (or, using the phonetic alphabet, X-ray, Yoke and Zulu or Zed) in order of increasing watertight security. In peacetime, condition X-ray meant that all doors, scuttles and valves were open, Yoke meant that all but the most essential of these were closed and Zulu meant that all such openings were shut. As war came, the

definitions, at least of condition X-ray, became more stringent. Every watertight opening was classified with one of the three letters indicating in which condition it should be closed. This meant that some doors, those marked X, would be kept closed at all times. The reason for keeping some openings permanently closed was the very real fear that time or opportunity would not be available to close them in an emergency:

'Unfortunately, there is the widespread misconception that doors and hatches between the still waterline and the actual waterline after surprise attack can be closed after attack, if repair parties and personnel are well trained.

'Experience has shown that doors and hatches which are not closed before the surprise attack are likely not to be closed for at least four reasons:

(1) The man detailed to close the door is likely to be disabled by the explosion.

(2) The bulkhead and door frame may be warped so that the door cannot close.

(3) The door itself or the door operating mechanism may be sprung.

(4) The door opening may be blocked by obstructions placed there by the explosion.

Left: The much larger starboard bulge added to *Saratoga* in early 1942 served many purposes. Here it acts as a diving platform for the crew at Kwajelein, February 1944. (NARA)

'It is to be borne in mind also that doors are a discontinuity and a source of structural weakness in bulkheads. The British have had a number of cases where a closed door, complete with its frame has been ripped completely free from the bulkhead by a heavy explosion.'[7]

In practice, however, a ship could not stay permanently in condition Zulu or even Yoke. The closing of doors and scuttles made the carrying out of normal activities difficult or impossible, and the shutting of valves sometimes cut off parts of the ship from drinking water or sanitary facilities.[8] The determination as to the condition set depended on where one was and when. Soon after the war began, Commander Pride commented:

'You cruise now in Condition Yoke - in fact, you're in Condition Yoke in Pearl Harbor, in a three-condition ship, and you go to Zed whenever you have general quarters. We tried the first day or two to keep Zed set a good part of the time and life around the ship just stopped. You can't get about the ship in Condition Zed. It's not advisable to set it anyway because you can't get to general quarters stations through it.'[9]

Later in the war *Saratoga* would normally set a hybrid condition, a combination of conditions X-ray and Yoke, when in a combat area but not actually at GQ.[10]

1. GenBd, BuCon -> SecNav, 18 July 1921, Armour Protection for Aeroplane Carriers (1st Endorsement). The endorsement is to a BuOrd memo dated 7 July 1921.
2. ibid.
3. BuCon, Sara -> BuCon, 17 December 1937, U.S.S. *Saratoga* (CV3) - Displacement and Battle Waterline.
4. BuCon, BuCon -> CinCUS, 11 May 1938, Displacement and Battle Waterline of Battleships, Airplane Carriers and Cruisers.
5. ibid. By the time the war began, nearly all the changes made to *Lexington* had been retrofitted in *Saratoga*, making the two ships almost equally heavy.
6. BuShips, NYPH -> Sara, 16 December 1941, U.S.S. *Saratoga* (CV3) - Recommendations to Improve Damage Control Arrangements and Ventilation. This was a complete examination of the state of damage control in *Saratoga*. On this subject the report said: 'In case of severe underwater damage the ship would take a quick list placing the second deck below the waterline and permitting water to flow through any holes opened in the side. It is imperative to prevent this water from spreading down to the third deck, inboard of the hangar bulkhead on the 2nd deck and fore and aft along the 2nd deck.'
7. ibid, p 3-4.
8. BuShips, Sara -> BuShips, 10 June 1944, U.S.S. *Saratoga* (CV3) - Alteration Request No. 34-44 (Install independent core valve in Wardroom Water Closet drain). *Saratoga* complained that in condition Zed, the wardroom heads became unusable because the water valves were shut.
9. BuShips, , 16 June 1942, Interview of Commander Alfred M. Pride, USN, in the Bureau of Aeronautics, p 9. The setting of condition Yoke in Pearl Harbor was obviously a

result of the fear that the Japanese would repeat the Pearl Harbor raid.

10. BuShips, Sara -> CinCPac, 10 September 1942, Action Report on Torpedoing of U.S.S. *Saratoga*, 31 August 1942.

3.2 Stability and Damage Control

Armour and watertight subdivision were the means by which damage due to enemy action was prevented or minimized. Stability and damage control were the active measures taken to maintain stability when the ship was intact and to control that stability and other damage when it had been hit.

Stability Control

It was known, even during the design stage, that the 'Lexingtons' would have an inherent list to starboard if they were evenly loaded.[1] This was because the island and funnel, both heavy structures, were positioned at the starboard edge of the flight deck on a hull intended for a symmetrical superstructure. The only way to keep the ship on an even keel, short of adding buoyancy to the starboard side, was to load consumables (e.g., fuel oil and feed water) in an asymmetrical manner. By loading approximately 800 tons less in the starboard tanks than in the port, the ship could be kept level.

The four layers of tanks that ran along most of the ships' sides were assigned functions by layer. The innermost layer was used to store reserve feed water and were known as the emergency reserve feed tanks; the next outboard layer stored fuel oil and were known as the fuel oil service tanks; the layer outside that also held fuel oil and were known as the fuel oil sluice tanks; and the outermost layer (wing tanks) held fuel oil as well and were known as the emergency fuel oil tanks. To load the ships with the maximum stable load (1,750,000gal of fuel oil – weighing approximately 6,000 tons) meant filling all four layers of tanks on the port side, while leaving the emergency reserve feed tanks and emergency fuel oil tanks empty on the starboard.[2] This solution was far from ideal particularly in view of the known overweight condition of the ships as war approached:

'If the ship were subjected to enemy attack (which might take place immediately upon leaving port) she might receive damage below the waterline on the starboard side. Resultant flooding would cause a further list to starboard and, there being no port tanks available for counter flooding due to all such tanks being full, the ship might capsize.

'The principal concern of the General

Board is that, when the vessel is subjected to enemy action, she be in condition effectively to resist and control damage. This condition is not reached until the top of the armoured belt is above water and counter flooding facilities are available.[3]

The problem was simply that the chronic overweight condition of the 'Lexingtons' dramatically reduced the options available to maintain or, more critically, regain stability.

When a ship takes on water on one side, the normal reaction, until it is possible to stop the flooding and pump the water overboard, is to add weight to the other side to compensate for any list caused by the flooding. This can be done either by pumping internal liquids from the flooded side to the dry side or, lacking available tanks or pumps, by counterflooding – the admission of external sea water to the dry side to balance the flooding. Obviously the former is preferable since it avoids contaminating oil or fresh water tanks with sea water; any tanks so flooded would then be unusable until they could be cleaned. The movement of internal liquids also poses problems since fuel oil is very thick and difficult to pump unless heated.

Because of the requirement to shift liquids from side to side, each of the tanks lining the outer shell of the lower hull was linked to a network of pipes and valves that crossed the hull at several points. By careful closing and opening of valves, this maze of pipes was divided into discrete systems for oil, feed water, drinking water and avgas. The actual movement of liquids was accomplished by pumps which were used in normal conditions to provide oil and feed water to the boilers, drinking water to the holding tank and avgas to the flight deck. To use these pumps for stability control, they and their valves had to be reset from their normal arrangement. In addition, void spaces had to be available, to fill with the liquids being transferred. In as-built, full-load condition, there were virtually no designed voids in the tank system. The wing tanks were fitted with the necessary facilities to be used in this capacity but were in fact designated for use as fuel oil tanks. Each of these twenty tanks had an 8in flood valve on the outer shell; hydraulically controlled from the wing tank control room, the valve could, in an emergency, be operated manually by reach rods. On the inboard bulkhead, each of these tanks had an oil suction valve through which it was filled and emptied.[4] In an emergency, oil could be pumped from these tanks to a void tank, if one were available, or blown overboard by high-pressure air.

To compensate partially for the weight of the island, nine wing tanks on the starboard side were in fact kept void. (The remaining starboard side wing tank and one tank on the port side, alongside the avgas tanks, were intended to be kept permanently void.) To prevent accidental contamination of these tanks by sea water, the flood valves on all the tanks were blanked. This elicited a complaint from *Saratoga* that it was impossible to train damage control teams as long as the flood valves were inoperative.[5] This proposal began a discussion on the merits of unblanking the sea valves. *Lexington* countered with the suggestion that only liquid transfer be practised, as counterflooding was a less complex operation.[6] BuCon endorsed a compromise, authorizing the unblanking of the sea valves on the ten starboard and one port void compartments and instructing that stability control be practised by pumping enough fuel from starboard to port to achieve a 5-deg list, and then counterflood the starboard voids to correct the list. Blanks were to be installed on the inboard suction valves to prevent any possible contamination.[7] This change had not been made in *Lexington* before the war began, although, apparently, the sea valve blanks had been removed in *Saratoga*.[8] *Lexington* complained bitterly that it was impossible for her to flood void compartments except by running a fire hose through the top manhole of the void and pumping water in from the fire mains. Not only was this inconvenient and slow, but it was impossible to perform in conditions Yoke or Zulu.[9]

In addition to the two layers of tanks on the starboard side left empty even at full load, other tanks were emptied as fuel was consumed. The established order of emptying tanks was:

'(1) Sufficient fuel is used from the sluice tanks in order to compensate for at least a 3deg list (approximately 90,000 gallons from each side). This leaves four of these tanks empty on each side.

'(2) Fuel oil tanks and bottoms forward of Frame 75 and fuel oil tanks and bottoms aft of Frame 133 are emptied simultaneously. These are emptied early in order to expedite refuelling.

'(3) The starboard and port sluice tanks are emptied simultaneously. These sluice tanks are used for removing list during damage control.

'(4) Reserve fuel oil bottoms are emptied. These bottoms are used as a standby to shift to in case the service fuel oil tanks become contaminated with salt water. This vessel becomes very sensitive to list and roll when these tanks are emptied.

'(5) Empty service tanks except the four used as fuel oil suction tanks.

'(6) Empty port emergency fuel oil tanks. Upon emptying these tanks, the vessel will list approximately 7deg to starboard even though the reserve feed water tanks and bottoms on the port side are full and those on the starboard side are empty.[10]

This emptying of tanks was a mixed blessing. Although it enabled stability to be maintained or regained through the transfer of liquids, it further compromised an already suspect protective scheme. Ever since coal was abandoned as the primary fuel for ships, ship designers have struggled to find a way to replace its protective power. A layer or two of coal bunkers around the outside of a hull was an ideal barrier against underwater blast damage, as from a torpedo. The real danger from such a blast is from the expanding gases. Coal provided room for the blast to dissipate; it crushed, absorbing much of the energy of the blast. Liquid fuels give no such advantage. In fact, a liquid filled tank acts simply as a shock-transmitter. A shock on the outside of such a tank is dissipated only to the degree to which it is distributed over the entire surface of the tank. Otherwise, the shock is simply passed through directly to the inner bulkhead. Thus, ship designers had to attempt to identify combinations of full and void tanks that would dissipate a torpedo's blast. Unfortunately, in the case of the 'Lexingtons', the need to empty two layers on the starboard and fill all layers on the port worked counter to the ideal protective scheme:

'While the ship is on an even keel, the use of fuel oil equally from each side would decrease the vulnerability by raising the armored belt and by making counter-flooding tanks available. However, the consumption of 1,600 tons, 800 from each side, of oil and consumable supplies would be necessary to bring the upper edge of the armoured belt and the third deck up to the waterline, and the consumption of an additional 1,600 tons will be required to raise the top of the armoured belt to 1ft above the waterline.

'As fuel is consumed, the side armour affords more protection. However, as the number of empty fuel oil tanks increases, the torpedo protection will decrease and the flooding of empty tanks due to a torpedo or mine would result in a greater list than would occur if the tanks were full of oil or water at the time of the explosion.'[11]

The ideal protective scheme called for a precise arrangement of filled and void tanks:

'The established principle of protection against contact explosion on a ship with underwater protection like the *Saratoga* requires: (a) a space next to the shell which may either be filled with liquid or void; (b) at least two layers of liquid to absorb the force of the explosion; (c) a void space in which the energy of the layer of liquid may be expended without damage to the protected vitals. It is understood that the difficulties of balancing the island structure make it impossible to adhere at all closely to these principles.'[12]

'The ideal condition would be for the present counter-flooding tanks to be empty and the remaining fuel oil tanks full with the top of the armoured belt about 1ft above the waterline. This condition cannot be realized without the installation of blisters of larger capacity than those presently installed.'[13]

The obvious solution was the installation of a bulge that would add buoyancy without requiring the asymmetrical filling of tanks. Group III of the 1938 'Circular of Requirements' called for the addition of just such a bulge on the starboard side, but, as with most of the other major changes called for in that document, this change was repeatedly postponed. The reason was concern about the length of time such a change would take and because the addition of the bulge would make it impossible for the 'Lexingtons' to traverse the Panama Canal.[14] *Saratoga* had her bulge installed during the major refit that followed her first torpedoing; *Lexington* was lost before her bulge could be fitted.[15]

Damage Control

Damage control, apart from stability control, means primarily the fighting of fires, although it also includes the physical repair of battle damage, particularly to the flight deck and watertight bulkheads. Firefighting was done primarily with water. A system of fire mains carried sea water to all decks and parts of the ship. Certain compartments were designed with special treatment due to the special characteristics of the space. These included the magazines which had overhead sprinklers and fast-flooding valves because these compartments obviously presented special danger. But the primary fire danger was perceived as being in the aircraft parked in the hangar or on the flight deck, possibly fuelled and armed. A 'water curtain' system was installed in the hangar, consisting of a series of transverse pipes in the overheads that were perforated by small, evenly spaced holes so as to create a wall of spray. The effect, it was

Right: Fire was the most frightening hazard in an aircraft-carrier, because there were so many combustible and explosive elements around. *Lexington* was lost to fire without suffering serious hull damage. When *Saratoga* was hit by Kamikazes on 21 February 1945, she had aircraft ready to launch on her forward catapults and others waiting their turn. These added significantly to the fires started by the Japanese attack. (NARA)

Left: The best weapon against avgas fire was foamite, a powdered soy bean derivative that was mixed with water and sprayed on the fire. Empty tins of foamite litter the deck after the fires were extinguished in this Hellcat in the middle of the flight deck forward. This aircraft is seen on fire in the middle of the previous photo. (NARA)

Left: A crewman has taken his foamite hose up to Pri-Fly on the inboard wing of the navigation bridge. (NARA)

Left: From the navigation bridge the hose was aimed into the open well of the forward elevator to fight the fires then raging in the hangar. (NARA)

hoped, would be to separate the large, open hangar into smaller, more manageable areas, the 'water curtain' preventing the spread of fire from one area to the next.

It was well known that water could not cope with the most serious types of fires likely in the 'Lexingtons'. Aircraft fires would probably involve burning avgas; water only serves to spread a petrol fire. To extinguish an avgas fire, it is necessary to smother it. For this purpose, the 'Lexingtons' were fitted with a foamite system. Foamite mixers were located in the boat pockets and the saluting gun platform. The foam was generated by mixing a soy-based powder into a stream of sea water pumped out at high pressure. The foam was intended to smother the fire by floating on the surface of the gasoline.[16] The foam generation system was highly effective when it worked, but it was not without its problems. In a test performed on *Saratoga* just after Pearl Harbor, the mechanism that fed the foamite powder from the hopper into the water stream became plugged to the extent that foam was blown back out of the hopper rather than out the hose.[17] Far more critical, however, was the problem of supplying foamite powder to the generators. The inspectors complained regularly that the ready supply on deck was inadequate and that resupply was difficult, heavy tins having to be hand-carried from supply rooms well below.

When flying operations were under way, a rescue man, known as a 'Hot Papa', was on duty. He wore an asbestos suit and carried a CO_2 fire extinguisher. His job, should an aircraft catch fire, was first to rescue the aircrew and then to fight the fire.[18]

Electrical fires, unlike petrol fires, could be fought with water, at least after the current had been switched off. Specific firefighting systems were built into the primary electrical equipment in the 'Lexingtons'. The main generators were equipped with a steam smothering system, in which steam from the adjacent boilers could be routed into the generator windings by perforated copper tubing. Lacking ready access to steam, the main motors used a fresh water spray system to achieve the same result. Neither system was much liked by the engineers because the windings in the generator or motor would become soaked with water, and even after the cause of the fire had been rectified, the machinery had to be thoroughly dried out, a slow and difficult operation, before it could be used again. As built, the 'Lexingtons'' only defence against electrical fires in other locations, apart from

water from the fire mains, was portable CO_2 fire-extinguishers located in the machinery spaces.[19]

Once a fire was under control, the major concern was for repair of damage, at least to the extent of shoring up watertight bulkheads and patching the flight deck. *Saratoga* reported on 20 March 1942 having three portable 200-amp motor-generator (DC) arc welding sets onboard but complained that they were too small and recommended that at least one be replaced by a 300-amp unit.[20] BuShips responded on 20 April 1942, making two transformer (AC) type 300-amp welding units available for *Lexington* at Pearl Harbor to be picked up at her next yard visit.[21] That visit was never to occur.

Damage control on the 'Lexingtons' was under the command of the first lieutenant, who directed operations from his command post at the central station on the first platform deck. His repair crews were organized into parties with specific responsibilities. The following describes the damage control organization in *Saratoga* in 1939 (*Lexington*'s organization differed in minor details only):

'Repair One is a deck repair party, manned and controlled by the Air Department. The headquarters for this party is located at the forward end of the stack structure in winch space, frame 88. The Air Officer controls this party through Fly I Officer...In the event that this party is driven below, it will occupy a station on the main deck at frame 45, and receive its orders direct from central station...This party handles all casualties on the main deck, flight deck, boat pockets, and in the superstructure.

'Repair Two is forward repair party, located in general workshop, compartment A-312-E. This party, which is supervised by a C&R department officer, is directly under the control of Central Station...This party handles all casualties on all decks below the main deck and forward of frame 75.

'Repair Three is the after repair party located in the after reserve plane stowage (D-322-A). A C&R officer is in charge of this repair party and receives orders directly from Central Station...This party is responsible for all casualties below the main deck and aft of frame 153.

'Repair Four is the forward engineering repair party with master station in the general workshop (A-312-E). This party is under the direct supervision of an engineering officer and receives normal orders direct from main control...In the event of certain casualties, orders can be sent direct from Central Station to repair four officer.

'Repair Five is boiler repair party. Master station is on the hangar deck, frame 121, at the after elevator. Communications are issued to this repair party via Main Control.

'Repair Six, ordnance repair party, is controlled through Central Station...The main station is at frame 55, third deck center-line, and can receive communications...from the Gunnery Officer. The secondary station, or the after station, is located at frame 154, third deck, and can be communicated with by Central Station direction...and by Gunnery Officer.'[22]

In addition to these major repair parties, *Saratoga* also had small battery repair units directly under the control of the Gunnery Department and a separate Air Department unit responsible for the gasoline system.

Practice versus Theory

The 'Lexingtons' suffered serious damage on four occasions during the war. The following describes each incident, detailing the damage and the damage control measures taken in each case:

Saratoga, 11 January 1942 – torpedoed northwest of Pearl Harbor (19°N, 165° 15'W) by *I-6*. One torpedo hit port side amidships (just forward of Frame 107). Boiler rooms 8, 10 and 12 were flooded as were three void tanks in the small port blister. There was no serious fire. Both counterflooding and the movement of internal liquids were used to control the resultant list. Five starboard fuel tanks (three wing tanks and two adjacent sluice tanks) which were void at the time were immediately flooded with sea water. The contents of eight port side oil tanks were then pumped to the starboard side. Once this was complete, the five counterflooded tanks were emptied overboard, leaving the ship with a slight starboard list.[23]

Lexington, 8 May 1942 – hit by two bombs and two torpedoes at the Battle of the Coral Sea. None caused apparently fatal damage. The bombs, in particular, caused only minor damage. One hit the flight deck port side forward, setting off some ready ammunition and bulging the deck slightly; the other hit the funnel, damaging the AA galleries located there. The only lingering effects of the bombs was a small, but persistent, fire in the wardroom officers' country on the main deck. One torpedo struck the port side forward in way of the avgas tanks; the second hit on the port side near the firerooms. The second did much more apparent damage, causing leakage in three boiler rooms, but this was soon controlled. The 6deg list that resulted from this hit was corrected within

Left: The bomb that hit the port side of *Lexington*'s flight deck during the Battle of the Coral Sea, 8 May 1942, did considerable damage to the forward 5in sponson on that side. Yet the effect on her seaworthiness and ability to fight from all four hits seemed minor. (NARA)

minutes by movement of internal liquids. The first torpedo caused minor local damage, but did disable the hydraulic system that powered both elevators, causing them to jam in place at the flight deck level. It also destroyed ventilation to a number of nearby compartments, including the forward IC room. The water-filled tanks outboard of the avgas had transmitted the shock of the torpedo blast directly to those tanks. While there was no apparent leakage from the port side tanks, the seams of the internal bulkheads had been distorted sufficiently to allow fumes to escape.

Approximately an hour and a half after the attack, when, except for the jammed elevators, *Lexington* seemed fully recovered from the attack and was ready to resume flying operations, the leaking avgas fumes reached the motor generators in the IC room. The resulting explosion at 1247 started immediate fires throughout the lower decks forward. Although she did not sink until well after dark, and then only after being scuttled, that explosion sealed her fate. The fires spread faster than damage control teams could contain them, fed by successive explosions as avgas fumes continued to leak into the ship. Further massive explosions at 1442 and 1525 led the first lieutenant to report, at 1538, that the fires were out of control. At 1707, the CO decided to get the crew off before approaching darkness made that a dangerous operation. The ship continued to burn fiercely until, glowing bright red from end to end, she was sunk by five torpedoes from the destroyer *Phelps*.

Saratoga, 31 August 1942 – torpedoed by *I-*

Right: Seen from *Enterprise*, *Lexington*, after the initial fires had been brought under control, appeared fully capable of continuing the fight. The only apparent effect of the hits was that she seemed to be slightly down by the bow. (NARA)

Right: Unseen, in the earlier views, was the avgas vapour that would explode with devastating effect. The damage caused by the original blast was irreversible, leading to increasingly frequent and damaging explosions that left *Lexington* settling by the bow and on fire from end to end. (NARA)

26 east of San Cristobal Island (10° 31'S, 164° 18'E), the southernmost of the Solomons chain. Hit by one torpedo on the starboard side at Frame 133, in way of boiler room 15 (the aftermost on that side). That boiler room flooded rapidly and leakage was reported in the adjacent boiler room 13. By 0933, approximately two hours after being torpedoed, the ship had a 6deg list to starboard. The outer three layers of port side water and fuel tanks were full, giving little opportunity to transfer liquids to correct the list. Nevertheless, the list was completely corrected within the next two hours without resorting to counterflooding. Eight small void tanks on the port side were filled with oil from the starboard, and two large oil tanks in the new starboard blister were simply emptied overboard. No fire was reported.[24]

Saratoga, 21 February 1945 – hit by four Kamikaze aircraft and by bombs from three other aircraft. The attacks started at 1700. The first Kamikaze crashed into the starboard side at Frame 104 and penetrated into the hangar, exploding there. The second hit the water at a low angle and skipped into the starboard side at Frame 147. The ship quickly took on a 5deg starboard list. The next attacker missed, crashing into the sea, but dropped bombs on the far forward flight deck, exploding in the anchor windlass space. This explosion knocked out the catapults and damaged the flight deck to the point that it was no longer usable forward. The next Kamikaze also hit the flight deck forward in the vicinity of the port catapult, among fuelled and armed Hellcats waiting to take off on night CAP, starting a fierce fire. The next hit the aircraft crane on the starboard side of the flight deck and fell over the side, but not before adding to the fire on the flight deck and in the starboard gun sponson. Sometime during this attack, a bomb or torpedo exploded along the starboard side at Frame 120 at the turn of the bilge, doing only minor damage. The

intensity of the attack was such (it lasted only three minutes) that this hit went unnoticed at the time. The fire on the flight deck was brought under control by 1814 and the hangar fire by 1830. A second attack began at 1846, resulting in one hit by a Kamikaze that struck the flight deck and slid over the port side, but its bombs exploded near Frame 42. This single hit caused little extra damage. The flight deck was completely demolished forward but was still operable aft and *Saratoga* was cleared to land aircraft again at 2015. Underwater damage proved minor and the list was controlled by the movement of internal liquids.[25]

1. GenBd, GenBd -> SecNav, 3 May 1922, Building Programme 1922 – Battle Cruisers 1 – 6 Class, converted to Airplane Carriers, p 2. The General Board noted that the converted aircraft-carriers would have a natural list of 7deg to starboard in normal condition with a symmetrical stowage of oil but that this could be corrected by distribution of oil or water ballast except when within 700 tons of maximum capacity.
2. BuShips, Lex -> CNO, 6 January 1942, Request for Decision as to the Best Operating Procedure for Obtaining Maximum Underwater Protection under present conditions on the U.S.S. *Lexington*.
3. BuShips, CNO -> BuShips, 19 April 1941, *Saratoga* (CV3), *Lexington* (CV2) - Improvement of Military Characteristics.
4. BuCon, Sara -> BuCon, 10 December 1934, U.S.S. *Saratoga* (CV3), Flooding Arrangements.
5. ibid.
6. BuCon, Lex -> BuCon, 31 January 1935, U.S.S. *Saratoga* (CV3), Flooding Arrangements (First Endorsement).
7. BuCon, BuCon -> ComAirBatFor, 20 March 1935, U.S.S. *Saratoga* (CV3), Flooding Arrangements (Third Endorsement).
8. BuShips, ComAirBatFor -> CNO, 10 January 1942, Request for Decision as to the Best Operating Procedure for Obtaining Maximum Underwater Protection under present conditions on the U.S.S. *Lexington* (First Endorsement).
9. BuShips, Lex -> CNO, 6 January 1942, Request for Decision as to the Best Operating Procedure for Obtaining Maximum Underwater Protection under present conditions on the U.S.S. *Lexington*. It should be noted that damage control was not the only reason for moving liquids. *Lexington* reported in this document that fuel had to be transferred to compensate for changes of

Left: Seen from an escort, *Saratoga* billows smoke from her bow, the result of the Kamikaze attack on 21 February 1945. Unlike *Lexington*'s, these fires were well contained in the upper decks and never threatened the ship. (NARA)

Above: Nevertheless, the damage at the bow destroyed both catapults and ripped large holes in *Saratoga*'s flight deck. This blow took her out of combat for the last time. (NARA)

weight when her air group was landing or launching and even when a stiff crosswind blew against the flat funnel structure.

10. ibid, p 6.

11. I&S, Report of Material Inspection of U.S.S. *Saratoga* (CV3) Held November 4-6, 1941 by Board of Inspection and Survey.

12. BuShips, NYPH -> Sara, 16 December 1941, U.S.S. *Saratoga* (CV3) - Recommendations to Improve Damage Control Arrangements and Ventilation.

13. op. cit.

14. BuCon, ComBatFor -> BuCon, 1 June 1939, Substitute for Installation of Blisters on *Lexington* and *Saratoga* during Modernization (First Endorsement).

15. *Lexington*'s loss was unrelated to her lack of the blister. *Saratoga*'s practice, with the blister, was to fill most of the blister tanks with oil, at least those in way of the

machinery spaces, while leaving the sluice tanks empty on that side for the same length. This meant that, from the outside in, she had two filled layers, a void layer, a filled layer and another void layer along most of the starboard side. On her port side, the small existing blister was left void, as was the inner layer of reserve feed water tanks. The intervening three layers were filled.

16. I&S, Report of Material Inspection of U.S.S. *Lexington* (CV2) Held 27, 28 and 29 October 1931 by Board of Inspection and Survey, p 66-7.

17. BuShips, NYPH -> Sara, 16 December 1941, U.S.S. *Saratoga* (CV3) – Recommendations to Improve Damage Control Arrangements and Ventilation, p 10.

18. Hook, Fall 1981, p 14.

19. I&S, Report of Material Inspection of U.S.S. *Lexington* (CV2) Held 27, 28 and 29 October 1931 by Board of Inspection and Survey, p 124.

20. BuShips, 31 March 42, Aircraft-carriers (CV2-3) (USS *Lexington* and USS *Saratoga*) – Welding Installations. *Saratoga*'s 20 March 1942 report is referenced in this document.

21. BuShips, BuShips -> Lex, 20 April 1942, U.S.S. *Lexington* (CV2) – Arc Welding equipment, transformer type - Installation and operation.

22. BuCon, This untitled and undated AirBatFor memo is in response to a 20 June 1939 letter from the senior member of the Interior Control Board to SecNav entitled USS *Lexington* and USS *Saratoga* (CV2 and CV3) - Modernization – Interior Control Requirements. It recommended a damage control organization with eight repair parties. Neither ship had that organization at the time of the memo, nor has this author been able to find any evidence that it was subsequently adopted.

23. BuShips, Sara -> BuShips, War Damage Report. There was a date on this document but it was unreadable on the carbon copy preserved in BuShips files. It was most likely written within a week or so of the torpedoing on 11 January 1942.

24. BuShips, Sara -> CinCPac, 10 September 1942, Action Report on Torpedoing of U.S.S. *Saratoga*, 31 August 1942.

25., BuShips, Sara -> CinCUS, 26 February 1945, U.S.S. *Saratoga* (CV3) Action Report for period 0900 (K) to 2130 (K), 21 February 1945 - forwarding of.

Right: Fire in a hangar could be even more dangerous than fire on the flight deck. Here the enclosing bulkheads keep the heat, and burning avgas, trapped inside. Not surprisingly, the aircraft stored there were gutted in the fires that resulted from the Kamikaze attack on *Saratoga*, 21 February 1945. (NARA)

4. Weapons Systems

When the 'Lexingtons' were being designed, the role they were to play as part of the fleet was far from clear. Were they to be purely platforms for aircraft, with a few guns only as defensive weapons, as envisaged by BuAer, or were they to act as scouts which just happened to carry aircraft? Lacking clairvoyance, the conservative naval leadership opted to arm the 'Lexingtons' as if they were heavy cruisers, giving them guns for offensive as well as defensive needs. It was also planned to install fixed underwater torpedo tubes, but these were deleted when it became necessary to trim weight from the hulls. The result of this process was that the 'Lexingtons' emerged with a wide variety of weapons systems, the make-up of which evolved over the years as the ships themselves evolved.

This chapter covers the evolution of the weapons themselves and of the control systems that allowed them to be used effectively. These control systems increasingly employed radar, which is dealt with in the next chapter.

4.1 Guns

8in Guns

The 'Lexingtons' were launched with a battery of eight 8in/55 Mk 9, Mod 1 guns in four twin mountings, paired two each fore and aft of the superstructure on the starboard side of the flight deck. The four mountings were numbered 1 to 4, from the bow. Internally the mountings were conventional. Powder and shell were passed to the upper handling rooms adjacent to each mounting's shallow barbette[1] and then through the barbette into the base of the mounting through a set of flameproof flaps. Once under the mounting, they were passed by hand up through a set of hinged trap doors where they were placed on loading trays and rammed home by a chain link rammer.[2]

Local fire control was provided at each mounting by an aimer's and layer's position at the top front of the mount. Each man had an armoured port through which he could observe the target. The two superfiring mountings had built-in rangefinders (Mk 30) at the aft end for use should local control become necessary. Fire control was normally provided by directors (General Electric Mk 18, Mod 1 and Mod 0) located in the 8in control tops fore and aft. These directors were generally satisfactory.[3]

From the ships' inception there was constant argument over the retention of these guns. Despite the arguments, the original guns were upgraded in November 1940 in *Lexington* with a new model (Mk 9, Mod 2). The commitment to the retention of the 8in battery went so far as to include the installation of FC (Mk 3) surface fire control radar on *Saratoga* during her late 1941

Left: No. 4 main battery mounting on *Saratoga*, 20 April 1936. These mountings were not heavily armoured, nor did they include any integral ammunition or powder hoists, so they were technically not turrets. (NHC)

refit.[4] Any plans for the main battery were superseded by the outbreak of war and *Saratoga*'s subsequent torpedoing:

'We got in and spent overnight getting fuel and bombs and ammunition out of the ship. Went into dry dock, patched her up and removed the turrets. We've been debating that question, as most of you know, ever since the ships were commissioned, whether they should be removed or not. Strange to say, our people had never been able to get a decision, but we had Admiral Leary aboard on that particular cruise. We had one day when the ship rolled and pitched very badly and he concluded that the turrets ought to come off right away. When we got in he went to see the

Commander-in-Chief, and in a very few days the turrets were off. It's rather unfortunate they jerked the barbettes and ammunition hoists out with them, because when we got back to Bremerton they concluded they would have the 5-inch twin mounts put on where the turrets had been, so they made new barbettes, just like the old ones, and stuck them back in and sent to Pearl Harbor for the ammunition hoists and stuck those back in and did a great deal of unnecessary work.'[5]

Lexington was due for a brief refit at Pearl Harbor shortly after that and CinCPac wanted to take advantage of that yard period to remove her 8in battery as well.[6] The ostensible reason for Nimitz's request was that the Army

Right: ComAirBatFor and his staff pose in front of No. 1 main battery on *Saratoga*, 30 May 1934. Note the canvas-covered sub-calibre gun mounted between the barrels of the 8in guns. This was used during target practice because it closely simulated the trajectory of the bigger gun and saved wear on the far more expensive 8in barrels. (NARA)

Right: *Lexington*'s No. 1 main battery mounting lowered on a wooden cradle on the barge used to transport the guns to their new coast defence site, 31 March 1942. Note the hoods in the forward face of the mounting for the aimer's and layer's positions in case local control was necessary. (NARA)

command on Oahu wanted *Lexington*'s main battery to supplement *Saratoga*'s, which was being set up as coast defence artillery, but the real reason was the need to beef up the AA battery. CNO approved CinCPac's request on 26 February 1942, instructing the yard at Pearl Harbor not to remove the ammunition hoists this time.[7] The mountings were removed from *Lexington* in four days, starting on 28 March 1942.[8]

5in Guns

The 'Lexingtons' were completed with a battery of twelve short 5in/25 Mk 10, Mod 1 guns in open mountings which were intended both as heavy AA weapons and as close-in defence against small craft. They were located three each in the four gun sponsons at main deck level at the bow and stern. Fire control was by four Ford Mk 19 Mod 1, 2 3 and 4 directors, each director controlling a battery of three guns. The Mk 19 director consisted of separate range/bearing and altimeter units mounted near each other on the 5in control tops. The range and bearing unit was based on an 8ft vertical coincidence rangefinder. These directors were generally unsatisfactory, being over-sensitive to shocks, vibration and variations in their 22-volt power supply; they were often knocked out of alignment by the act of firing the main battery.[9]

The 1938 'Circular of Requirements' called for the modernization, but not the replacement, of the existing 5in battery. The mountings were to be modernized, motorized and given Thyratron-type remote control. At the same time, plans were made to replace the now obsolete Mk 19 directors with an equal number of modern Mk 33 lightweight directors equipped with integral 15ft stereoscopic rangefinders.[10] BuCon protested against the weight and space that four of these directors would take up and compromised with BuOrd on two Mk 33 directors, one each on the fore and aft 5in fire control tops.[11] It was also planned to cut large indentations in the flight deck so that the 5in guns could be fired across the deck at any elevation greater than 40deg.[12] Thus the guns at one corner of the flight deck could help those in the adjacent section in at least part of their coverage. These plans went so far as the letting of contracts by BuOrd for the Mk 33 directors and for the Thyratron remote control gear for the individual gun mountings, but this particular set of changes was never to be made.[13]

Lexington was never to have major changes made to her 5in gun battery. The proposed

Above: *Lexington*'s No. 3 mounting being lifted off the ship, 30 March 1942. This, and the forward superfiring mounting, had an integral rangefinder at the rear. (NARA)

changes to both ships were repeatedly postponed in the last years before war broke out.[14] The only planned change for *Lexington* was the replacement of the twelve gun barrels in May 1942 because the originals were worn and losing velocity due to erosion, and the more nebulous plan of installing the long-planned Mk 33 directors during that year.[15] At the outbreak of war, *Saratoga* differed only in that her 5in gun barrels had already been recently replaced. The two ships would soon, briefly, differ by quite a bit. *Lexington* fought her war, until her loss in May 1942, with her 5in battery unchanged; *Saratoga* would have hers completely revised as a side-effect of her torpedoing and the subsequent removal of her 8in main battery.

The idea of not only modernizing the 5in battery but also upgrading it at the same time seems to have originated as a long-term extension of the general programme of adding remote control and better directors to the existing battery.[16] However, within a month the plan to replace the 5in/25 battery with newer, longer-range 5in/38s became reality. Once the decision had been taken to remove the 8in main battery, the rest followed logically. The only

the short 5in guns in the sponsons to simplify maintenance and ammunition supply. Because of the greater weight and size of the new guns, two would replace three on each of the sponsons.[17] Thus, *Saratoga* emerged in late May 1942 with sixteen 5in/38s, eight in twin mountings and eight single guns. Fire control was completely revised as well. The 5in battery was controlled by two new Mk 37 directors located in the new sky forward and sky aft, each director controlling half the battery. Each had an associated Mk 1 fire-control computer and FD (Mk 4) fire-control radar. Control in the single mountings was by a match needle system in which the Mk 1 computer set pointers in both elevation and train, and the local gun crew followed manually. All mountings had automatic fuse-setters. (The desire for complete remote control of the single mountings had not disappeared; it simply was put on hold due to the lack of availability of the Thyratron equipment.)[18] Under this system, unless only one target was present forward or aft, some of the 5in guns would be operated under purely local control, since each Mk 37 could track only one target at a time.

The new 5in battery became part of the cause of *Saratoga*'s missing the pivotal Battle of Midway. She had originally been scheduled to complete her refit on 13 May 1942, but while undergoing final tests of her new battery, a 5in round exploded in the barrel of the left gun of No. 4 mounting, damaging it so severely that it had to be replaced.[19] As a result of this accident, *Saratoga* did not leave Puget Sound until 22 May.[20] The nine-day delay was sufficient to

Above: Looking aft along *Lexington*'s starboard forward AA sponson, 27 July 1928. Three 5in/25 single mountings were carried on each of four sponsons. This was a low-velocity weapon optimized for rapid firing and ease of training. Above the sponson was the aircraft crane, resting on the deck to clear the arc for the forward main battery mountings. (NARA)

Right: Close-up of the foretop on *Saratoga* at the time of her commissioning, 16 November 1927. The port side 5in altimeter, half of the Mk 19 director for that side, can be seen in the foreground. The other half, the range/bearing unit, is out of the picture to the left. (NARA)

reasonable replacement for the 8in mountings were 5in/38 twin mountings which had become the standard heavy DP armament in the Navy's newest battleships, cruisers and aircraft-carriers. As long as the new, longer 5in gun was being introduced, it made sense to replace

cause her to miss the battle as she had to pass through San Diego to pick up a cargo of aircraft for Pearl Harbor. She did not reach Pearl Harbor until 6 June, two days after the decisive battle!

Saratoga's 5in battery remained unchanged for the rest of the war. Prior to her final disposition, however, exactly half her 5in battery was removed to reduce top weight. Photographs taken at Alameda, CA, in February 1946 show one single mounting removed from each sponson and Nos. 2 and 4 mountings deleted.

Until the development of guided weapons, anti-aircraft defence relied primarily on sheer numbers of projectiles to destroy attacking aircraft before they could get close enough to do damage. Even with radar guidance, as was provided by the Mk 37 director with FD radar, the chances of hitting an attacking aircraft with any one weapon were far too small. Thus the number and type of AA weapons carried on attractive targets, such as the 'Lexingtons', increased dramatically as war began. The 5in battery represented the heavy end of the spectrum of AA weaponry (with the light and medium AA weapons, described in the next section, making up the balance). Unlike lighter weapons, which counted on rapid fire and multiple hits to do damage, the 5in gun fired far more slowly, but put a far heavier shell in the air. The standard 5in shell, with which the US Navy started the war, weighed 55.18lb, of which 7.55lb was explosive charge. The shell was detonated by contact with a target, a very rare occurrence, or by time fuse. A shell that exploded near enough to a target might be able to do sufficient damage through blast and shrapnel to deflect it from its course. The fuse would be set to explode at the anticipated altitude of the target, which could be calculated using the known angle of the barrel and the known time to altitude of the shell when fired at that angle. The actual setting was done in the bank of automatic fuse-setters located near the breech of the gun. The shell, an 'all-up' round consisting of projectile and powder charge, was placed nose-down in the fuse-setter until ready to fire. A man sat on the left side (of the single mounting), entering the desired altitude into the bank of fuse-setters. Then, as the gun was pointed at various angles, the fuse setting was automatically updated until the round was removed from the fuse-setter just before firing.

The first faltering step towards 'Smart' weaponry came with the introduction of the proximity fuse (known to the British as the

influence fuse). This was a joint development by the British and Americans, the original work on the photo-electric cell being done in the USA by Western Electric and RCA, and much of the experimental work of turning it into a useful fuse being done by Dr. Aylwin Crow in England.[21] The principle was that the shell was aimed so that, if it did not hit, it would miss just under the target. The shadow cast by the target would interrupt the current generated by the photo-electric cell in the fuse, which could be used to detonate the shell. Dr. Crow found initially that the fuse was far too fragile to be put in an artillery shell and did his experiments with unguided rockets. Even then, the initial batches were erratic at best. The American liaison officer reported:

> 'They were having trouble with arming. The fuse would be too sensitive and would go off prematurely if the rocket wobbled. If there was a cloud which passed over the sun it might go off, or if it ran into a raindrop it might...the shoulder was just a little bit too high so that as the rocket wobbled a little bit, the light would change, this shoulder would cast a shadow on the cell and it would go. They figured about 25 per cent were prematures, even then, and about 25 per cent might get to the target and operate against it. The others would go beyond and, hopefully, self-destruct. A fuse had two arming devices: one to arm the fuse after about a second and one to explode the fuse after it had passed the target so that it would not hit your own ship's troops.'[22]

This fuse was eventually fitted to the 5in shell, in which guise the shell was known as a VT round.

Above: The twelve 5in/25s in the AA sponsons were replaced by eight larger and newer 5in/38 base ring mountings on *Saratoga*. This view dates from 9 September 1945. Note the bank of fuse-setters on the right. The gun captain, at far right, is connected by telephone to the AA plotting room below decks. These were simply destroyer mountings with the gunhouse and all hoists removed. (NARA)

Above: When *Saratoga's* main battery was removed, its place was taken by four 5in/38 twin mountings, 14 May 1942. Note the open gun captain's position, protected only by the railing on top of each gunhouse. (USN via Baker)

Saratoga's report of her action against the Kamikazes on 21 February 1945 showed that 494 Mk 32 VTs were fired compared with 223 standard (Mk 18) 5in rounds. She was far from pleased with the performance of the VT, complaining that an estimated 25-30 per cent exploded prematurely when only 200-300 yards from the muzzle.[23]

AA Weapons

Photographic evidence indicates that the 'Lexingtons' were completed with no dedicated AA weapons. Positions had been created for a single .50cal machine-gun on the roof of Nos. 2 and 3 8in mountings, but they had not been installed by the time the ships were launched. They were in place, however, by the time of *Lexington's* first major inspection in 1931. At that time, the inspectors supported the ship's desire to install ready ammunition storage boxes near the guns on the roofs of the superfiring mountings. By 1935 the need for more AA guns had reached the point that *Lexington* was taken in hand and fitted with five new gun platforms. Four of these were at the corners; these platforms were each designed to carry four .50cal machine-guns, although the exact number and type of guns carried on these platforms varied. The other platform was at the fifth level of the funnel. This platform wrapped all the way around the funnel, and six .50cal guns were mounted on each side. The .50cal guns that were mounted elsewhere on

Lexington were removed at the same time.[24]

Saratoga was also intended to receive these platforms but never did. Instead, she received more .50cal guns in a piecemeal fashion. For example, during her 1933-34 overhaul the twin .50cal mounting on the roof of No. 2 8in mount was replaced by two single .50cal Mk 3s, while the older twin mounting on No. 3 was retained.[25] *Saratoga* complained that the new battery on No. 2 8in mount interfered with vision forward from the conning tower and made too much noise when fired, but ComBatFor commented that she was scheduled shortly to receive her full complement of 24 machine-guns (presumably on platforms similar to *Lexington's*) and in the meanwhile she could tolerate the inconvenience.[26] CinCUS injected reality into the debate, noting that the Navy had run out of money and plans to add AA to *Saratoga* were on indefinite hold, so she would retain her present battery of .50cal guns.[27] In 1939 *Saratoga* complained bitterly that she had only four machine-guns. The old twin mounting on No. 3 8in mounting had apparently been removed, because *Saratoga* now had only the two single mountings on No. 2 and two other single mountings, not permanently sited, that could be set up on the flight deck by the crew if air operations were not in progress.[28]

There was some rearrangement of *Lexington's* .50cal machine-guns in October 1940 when 3in/50 single mountings were added to the corner platforms in place of two .50cal guns on each. The eight displaced machine-guns were sited, two each, on top of the four 8in turrets.[29] In August 1941 when *Saratoga* had her flight deck widened forward, she appears to have had a number of small AA platforms added to the roof of the pilot house on the island and at the level of the main battery control top on the aft face of the funnel.[30] *Lexington* appears to have had platforms for .50cal guns added to her former aft main battery control top after the 8in guns and their directors had been removed.[31]

While the light AA battery of the 'Lexingtons' was being expanded, it had become clear to the Navy that a heavier, rapid-firing weapon was needed. The .50cal machine-gun was a popular weapon, being fast-firing and extremely reliable, but it was simply too light a weapon to be effective against ever faster and heavier targets. As early as 1933, BuOrd was working on a 1.1in quadruple machine-gun to supplement the lighter .50cal. The bureau reasoned that the 1.1in would be at least twelve times as effective as a single-barrel .50cal since they would have the same effective rate of fire (counting the 1.1's four barrels against the .50's one) and the lighter weapon would have to hit a vital area on the aircraft (approximately one-twelfth of the presented area of the machine) while the heavier weapon would be effective hitting anywhere on the target.[32] The development of the 1.1in machine-gun was slow, however, and it was not until 1940 that definite plans were made to install four quadruple mountings on each of the 'Lexingtons'.[33] As the scheduled time for *Lexington*'s late-1940 yard period approached, instructions were issued to install five unpowered 1.1in quadruple guns without director control. Foundations were to be installed for the later addition of Mk 45 directors; power drive for the mountings was also to be added at some time in the future. *Saratoga*, which was not scheduled for overhaul until 1941, was intended to receive a similar number of power-operated 1.1s with temporary control by Mk 44 directors until the more capable Mk 45 became available.[34] However, when *Lexington* actually entered Puget Sound for her refit in October 1940, the 1.1s were not available and she was given five 3in/50 Mk 10 Mod 2 single mountings, one each at the corners and one on a new platform on the roof of the small deckhouse on the flight deck between the island and the funnel. Almost a year later, when *Saratoga* underwent her long-delayed refit in August 1941, the 1.1s were still

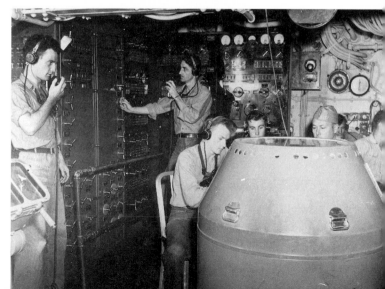

unavailable and she received five 3in/50s in four new small corner sponsons and on the deckhouse between the island and funnel.[35] These guns were capable of semi-automatic operation, but were never used in that mode because the loading cycle was mistimed, causing the breech block to close prematurely.[36]

Even without these problems, the 3in gun would have been only a temporary replacement for the planned 1.1in quadruple machine-guns; they were too slow-firing, even if the semi-automatic mode had worked as planned, to be an effective medium AA weapon. As soon as 1.1s became available, they were substituted for the 3in mountings. On *Saratoga* this took place during a short yard visit to Bremerton in late November 1941 – which caused her to be absent from Pearl Harbor during the Japanese attack. *Lexington* had already made the substitution in August 1941.[37] When *Lexington*'s main battery was removed in March 1942, there were no immediate plans to replace it with 5in twin mountings as was already being done for *Saratoga*. Instead, *Lexington* was to receive seven further 1.1in mountings in addition to the five already onboard. The new guns, together with the existing deckhouse mounting, were to be sited, two each, in the place of the now-removed 8in turrets. Four directors, one for each pair of 1.1s in the new battery, were to be installed.[38] In the

event, the directors, and the planned power units for the new and old mountings, were unavailable and were not installed.[39] Time did not allow the deckhouse 1.1in to be relocated. Thus, only three 1.1s were sited aft of the funnel in the old main battery positions, although four were added forward as planned.[40]

At the same time, *Lexington* was to have been fitted with at least eighteen new 20mm Oerlikon in single mountings.[41] This was the gun that had been selected as the new standard light AA weapon. The desire to replace the .50cal machine-gun as the light AA gun was understandable, given the light weight of its round and its relatively short range. Nevertheless, there seemed to be no acceptable substitute available; certainly none had been developed in the USA. In this case, the British conveniently supplied the solution:

'The British actually started to mass-manufacture the Oerlikon in the US before we took it over. Then we drained off part of their production and got other factories to produce it. As I remember, the automobile companies, and General Electric, and other manufacturers in the country who did not build ordnance were in on building the Oerlikon.'[42]

In the brief yard period that followed the removal of her main battery, *Lexington* had four new AA galleries installed: one at flight deck level outboard of the funnel, another in the starboard side boat pocket and two in port side boat pockets (the first and third from the bow on that side). The boat pocket platforms were hinged so they could fold upwards. A total of 22 single 20mm mountings were added: six in the new funnel gallery, five in the starboard boat pocket gallery, seven divided between the two port side boat pocket galleries (four in the forward pocket and three in the after), two on the old aft main battery director top and two right aft (at Frame 212) at the corners of the flight deck.[43] Thus *Lexington* left Pearl Harbor in April 1942 armed with twelve 5in/25s, twelve 1.1in quadruple machine-guns and 22 20mm Oerlikons. It is not clear what happened to the 0.50s displaced by the removal of the main battery, but at least four were sited on the new flight deck level funnel gallery. In addition to the AA battery just listed, *Lexington* mounted at least 24 0.50in machine-guns at the time of her loss.

When *Saratoga* entered Puget Sound for repairs in February 1942, more was done to upgrade her AA outfit than upgrading her 5in battery. The vacant space on each of the 5in gun

Above: *Lexington*'s AA battery was strengthened before the war by extra sponsons at each bow and quarter and by the funnel platform. During her brief yard visit at Pearl Harbor in late March 1942, she had three extra 1.1in quads installed in place of her recently removed main battery and 22 new 20mm mountings, eleven of them in two new galleries in the starboard boat pocket and at the base of the funnel. This photo shows her just before the avgas explosions that caused her loss. (NHC)

Left: When *Saratoga* was refitted in early 1942 she was to have received nine 40mm mountings, but these were not available and she left the yard with nine 1.1in quads, one of which can be seen at the forward end of the 5in AA sponson, filling the space left when two 5in/38s took the place of three 5in/25s, 14 May 1942. (NARA)

Left: *Saratoga* also received 20mm mountings on the outside of her funnel, but these, unlike *Lexington*'s, were given individual gun tubs, 14 May 1942. Note that each mounting has a complex guard welded above it, preventing the barrel from swinging into a position in which it could shoot the funnel or one of the other guntubs. (NARA)

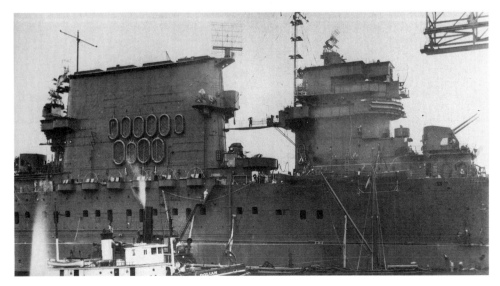

sponsors (left when two 5in/38s replaced three 5in/25s) and the space left after removing the five 1.1in mountings was to be filled with a new medium AA gun. The 1.1in quad had proved to be a failure in use:

'Then we had the 1.1in, which had been developed by the Bureau of Ordnance, a very good gun, but too finely precisioned, so that once you got it afloat with sailors and salt air, it was always giving trouble. Most in the fleet didn't like it. Anybody who knew, who was very careful with it and trained his people well, got good results. But few liked it. So they had been looking for another weapon for mid-range firing. The 1.1in would be about a 30mm, and the British had developed their multi-barrelled pom-pom, about a 40mm. They called it the "walking piano" because it was very loosely constructed, and worked under almost any conditions, but they didn't have suitable fire control and we didn't either. Nobody had a fire control for these short-range weapons then. So the 1.1 and the 20mm were our interest for immediate installation.'[44]

The Navy had decided that the gun to replace the 1.1in was the Swedish 40mm Bofors, available in twin and quadruple mountings.[45] But supplies were not yet reaching the dockyards,

so when *Saratoga* left the yard at Bremerton in late May 1942, she carried, as well as the sixteen 5in/38s, a total of nine 1.1in quadruple mountings (the five that were there before and one each on the 5in gun sponsons) and 32 20mm single mountings disposed as follows: four (two on each side) in aftward extensions of the bow 1.1in gun sponsons; six in single guntubs at flight deck level on the starboard side of the funnel; four in a gallery at the port edge of the flight deck, centred on Frame 91, across the flight deck from the forward edge of the funnel; four in a similar gallery centred on Frame 129, across the flight deck from No. 3 5in twin mounting; four in a gallery on the starboard edge of the flight deck at Frame 150, aft of No. 4 5in twin mounting; eight along the flight deck aft, four on each side, centred on Frame 203; and two in single guntubs facing aft under the flight deck round-down.[46]

The 1.1in mountings were director-controlled and electrically powered. The directors were the first of their type for smaller calibre weapons and had been developed in record time. Rear Admiral Eller, then temporarily on BuOrd staff, was involved in the testing of the new director along with its creator, Dr. Stark Draper of MIT:

Below: An excellent view of *Saratoga*'s new bridge structure, 14 May 1942, showing the arrangement of Sky Forward built on top of the flag bridge, the 1.1in quad mounting sited between the island and the funnel, and the new wings added to either side of the CXAM room on the forward face of the funnel, each one holding a searchlight. (USN via Baker)

'What we needed for the Bofors was proper fire control because we still had, even for the 1.1, the old eye sights like those on a rifle or a machine-gun. We needed something that would calculate the movement of a plane and introduce lead and proper elevation and range...He [Dr. Draper] was developing the first air-spun gyro, which became the heart of the fire control system...Finally, he got the gyro perfected to the point that we installed it in what we call a "breadboard model" of a sight, took it down to Dahlgren [the US Navy's gunnery test range at Dahlgren, VA] and mounted it on a 20-millimetre. I went along, having had so much experience in firing .50-calibre and in tracer control. We fired it with tracers to check the sight against a fast towed target. I used the sight as it had been developed by BuOrd, incorporating his gyro. It worked so much better than tracer control that I said, "Take it. Go ahead and develop it." Nobody else knowing much about it, they did go ahead and develop it. Years later...we were talking about this, and he said that was the quickest he had ever seen anything done in the Navy.'[47]

Despite the improvement that director control made in the accuracy of the 1.1in gun, it could not overcome the basic problem of unreliability, now only compounded by the electric drive system.[48] It was clear that the 1.1s would be replaced by Bofors at the first opportunity. The Japanese provided this opportunity by torpedoing *Saratoga* again in August 1942, sending her back to the yard at Pearl Harbor. This was a relatively quick visit and no major structural changes were made. The nine 1.1s were replaced with an equal number of 40mm

quads, together with five new Mk 51 directors, replacing the earlier directors used with the 1.1. The big change, however, was the further increase in the 20mm battery, now 52 in single mountings, arranged as follows: nine in a continuous gallery outboard of the funnel at flight deck level (replacing the six there previously); four (two on each side) at the bow as before; seven in individual guntubs on the port side, between the 5in sponson and the existing midships port side gallery, centred on Frame 72; six in the midships port gallery, the existing gallery being extended aft to add two mountings; four in the second port gallery, as before; four in the existing starboard gallery aft of No. 4 5in mounting; two in the starboard side boat pocket, directly below the existing starboard gallery; twelve aft along the flight deck, eight as before with three more added to the starboard side by extending that sponson aft and one more added to port in a single guntub; and four (two on each side) right aft at the round-down.[49]

Saratoga's AA fit remained stable after the late-1942 refit until her next scheduled refit, which took place in January 1944, at Hunters Point, California. This refit saw a dramatic increase in the 40mm battery with a corresponding decrease in the 20mm fit. The 40mm battery increased to 23 quadruple mountings and two twins. All nine existing mountings were retained and the following were added: two quadruple mountings (one on each side, just aft of the existing forward mounting), displacing a pair of 20mm guns on each side; two twin mountings on the port side at Frame 72, displacing a gallery for seven

Above: *Saratoga*'s medium and light AA batteries were significantly improved after her repair in the autumn of 1942. Note the multiple galleries of single 20mm mountings now lining her flight deck, 12 November 1942. The nine 1.1in quads have now been replaced by an equal number of 40mm quads. (NARA)

Above: When *Saratoga* was next refitted, in early 1944 at Hunters Point, her medium AA outfit was greatly increased at the expense of her 20mm battery. Some of the new (and old) 40mm guns and their associated controllers on her port side are circled in this pair of dockyard views taken on 2 January 1944. (NARA)

20mm guns previously mounted there; seven quadruple mountings in the port side boat pockets, two each in the first, second and fourth, one in the third, displacing ten 20mm mountings in two flight deck galleries along the port side; three quadruple mountings outboard of the funnel on the starboard side, displacing nine 20mm guns; and two quadruple mountings in the starboard boat pocket, displacing two 20mm guns in the pocket and four along the flight deck above it.[50] The sixteen remaining 20mm were as before. None of *Saratoga*'s remaining refits altered her AA outfit significantly until after the war, when it was drastically reduced to cut topweight and regain stability.

1. The reason why these mountings were called mountings and not turrets was because of the shallowness of the armoured barbettes and the fact that the mountings included almost no integral ammunition handling gear.
2. I&S, 4 November 1931, Report of Material Inspection of U.S.S. *Lexington* (CV2), Held 27, 28 and 29 October 1931, p 133-9.
3. ibid, p 139.
4. BuShips, NYPS -> BuShips, 27 November 1941, Naval Message 270420.
5. BuShips, 16 June 1942, Interview of Commander Alfred M. Pride in the Bureau of Aeronautics, p 6. The removal of the 8in battery was followed, during the subsequent major rebuild at NYPS, by the removal of the FC radar.
6. BuShips, CinCPac -> CinCUS, 1 February 1942, Naval Message 010253.
7. BuShips, CNO -> CinCPac, 26 February 1942, Naval Message 261930.
8. BuShips, NYPH -> BuShips, 14 April 1942, USS *Lexington* (CV2) - Removal of 8in Battery.

9. I&S, 4 November 1931, Report of Material Inspection of U.S.S. *Lexington* (CV2), Held 27, 28 and 29 October 1931, p 137-9.

10. The Mk 33 director was being fitted to the Navy's 8in gunned Treaty cruisers because they, like the 'Lexingtons', were greatly overweight and the Mk 33 weighed considerably less than the more capable Mk 37.

11. BuCon, Circular of Requirements for the Modernization of the USS *Lexington* and USS *Saratoga*.

12. BuCon, BuCon -> NYPS, 3 November 1939, USS *Lexington* (CV2) and USS *Saratoga* (CV3) – Modernization of – Group XX - Changes in Flight Deck to permit firing of 5in – 25 cal. A.A. guns across vessel at elevation of 40˚.

13. BuShips, 21 May 1940, Specifications for Modernization of Antiaircraft Battery Fire Control USS *Saratoga* and USS *Lexington*.

14. BuShips, NYPS -> BuShips, 13 November 1940, U.S.S. *Saratoga* (CV3) – Battle Telephone System - Sound Powered Switchboard Type - Revision of. This seemingly unrelated document contains the following relevant passage: 'Since *Saratoga* may be expected to retain the four present 5in directors and altimeters indefinitely together with the present arrangement of four groups of three 5in guns each.'

15. I&S, , 5 September 1941, U.S.S. *Lexington* (CV2) - Material Inspection of, p VII-1-5.

16. BuShips, NYPS -> BuShips, 8 January 1942, USS *Lexington* (CV2) and USS *Saratoga* (CV3) - Fire Control Modernization Projects. This document mentions the plan to upgrade the 5in battery to 5in/38s under the heading of 'Long range program'.

17. BuShips, BuShips -> NYPS, 14 February 1942, Naval Message 142100. The single mountings were really destroyer-type base ring mountings (Mk 30) with the removal of the enclosing shield and all hoisting gear that extended below the base ring.

18. BuShips, CNO -> BuOrd, 29 January 1942, U.S.S. *Saratoga* (CV3) - Re-armament of.

19. BuShips, Sara -> ComAirPac, 13 May 1942, Naval Message 130555. The cause was apparently a defective Mk 35 AAC projectile.

20. BuShips, NYPS -> ComServPac, 13 May 1942, Naval Message 131847.

21. Oral, Eller Interview No. 7, p 382-3. The American effort was led by Dr. Merle Tuve.

22. Oral, Eller Interview No. 8, p 451-2.

23. BuShips, Sara -> CinCUS, 26 February 1945, U.S.S. *Saratoga* (CV3) Action Report for the period 0900 (K) to 2130 (K), 21 February 1945.

24. BuCon, Sara -> BuOrd, 12 Oct 1935, .50 Cal. Machine Gun Installation, disposition of.

25. ibid.

26. BuCon, ComBatFor -> BuOrd, 2 November 1935, .50 Cal. Machine Gun Installation, disposition of (3rd Endorsement).

27. BuCon, CinCUS -> BuOrd, 8 November 1935, .50 Cal. Machine Gun Installation, disposition of (4th Endorsement).

28. BuCon, Sara -> ComCarDivOne, 21 September 1939, .50 calibre Anti-Aircraft Machine Gun Battery and Fire Control Searchlights. In this letter *Saratoga* requested that at least some of the now 28 authorized mgs be installed during her next overhaul.

29. BuShips, Lex -> BuShips, 17 August 1940, .50 calibre machine guns, removal of.

30. The only evidence for these platforms is in the alteration notes attached to the 27 April 1944 plans of *Saratoga*. The author has found no photographic evidence to back up these notes.

31. The use of the word 'appears' in the last two sentences is deliberate. The author has been able to find no solid documentary evidence outlining the rapid changes in the .50 cal battery during 1941 and early 1942. The only clues are hints, such as the fact that *Lexington* had 34 .50s in September 1941 (noted in the inspection done then) and the few poor-quality photographs showing the ships during this period.

32. GenBd, BuOrd Memorandum, 7 November 1933, .50 Cal. – 1.1.

33. BuShips, , 21 May 1940, Specifications for Modernization of Antiaircraft Battery Fire Control USS *Saratoga* and USS *Lexington*.

34. BuShips, BuShips -> NYPS, 25 August 1940, USS *Lexington* (CV2), USS *Saratoga* (CV3) 1.1 Mount - External Wiring of.

35. BuShips, Sara -> BuShips, 15 August 1941, Construction of RADAR Plotting Room, Request for. The location of the No. 3 3in mounting on the deckhouse between the island and funnel was severely criticized as having a very limited arc of fire. *Saratoga* wanted to build a radar plotting compartment where the gun was sited.

36. I&S, , 5 September 1941, U.S.S. *Lexington* (CV2) - Material Inspection of, p VII-2.

37. BuShips, Lex -> ComCarDivOne, 28 August 1941, Construction of Radar Plot Room in U.S.S. *Saratoga* - Request for.

38. BuShips, OpNav -> CinCPac, 26 February 1942, Naval Message 261930.

39. BuShips, NYPH -> BuShips, 19 March 1942, USS *Lexington* -20mm and 1.1 Installation. This letter detailed the planned AA installation for *Lexington*.

40. BuShips, NYPH -> BuShips, 17 April 1942, USS *Lexington* - Antiaircraft Battery. This letter detailed where the actual fit varied from the plan. It mentioned in passing that the twelve power units and four directors had finally arrived and would be available for *Lexington*'s next yard visit.

41. ibid.

42. Oral, Eller Interview No. 9, p 498. The Oerlikon was a Swiss design that was being manufactured under licence in the USA for the British.

43. BuShips, NYPH -> BuShips, 17 April 1942, USS *Lexington* - Antiaircraft Battery.
BuShips, NYPH -> BuShips, 1 May 1942, U.S.S. *Lexington* (CV2) – Installation of 20 MM and 1.1 A.A. Guns.

44. Oral, Eller Interview No. 9, p 491-2.

45. Oral, Eller Interview No. 9, p 497. '..they had already got from the Dutch down in the West Indies, a Dutch cruiser I believe, the plans for the Bofors, a Swedish gun that the Dutch had bought. So we went ahead and were building the Bofors then. We were just starting to... I think we just went ahead and made the formal arrangements afterwards...'

46. The reference for this data is a set of BuShips plans, No. 112352, undated, but obviously showing *Saratoga* as she looked after this refit.

47. Oral, Eller Interview No. 9, p 498-500.

48. Oral, Eller Interview No. 9, p 505-6. During this period, Eller was gunnery officer in *Saratoga* and complained about the electric drive. 'All my time on board we were working on trying to iron out the bugs in the electric drive. It had been rushed through the factory too fast before testing and properly working up...'

49. BuShips, NYPH -> BuShips, 10 November 1942, USS *Saratoga* (CV3) – Weight Changes Incidental to Armament Alterations.

50. BuShips, Sara -> BuShips, 8 March 1944, USS *Saratoga* (CV3) - Alteration Request No. 11-43 and 12-43.

4.2 Aircraft

The 'Lexingtons'' primary weapon, both offensive and defensive, was their air groups. This section describes the handling of those air groups on and around the aircraft-carriers. The first two sub-sections describe the physical features of the hangar and flight decks related to aircraft; the last sub-section discusses aircraft handling in general.

Hangar Deck

The hangar on the 'Lexingtons' was a large open space used primarily for the repair and maintenance of aircraft. The original conception of aircraft-carrier operations had included the use of the hangar as a storage location for ready aircraft, thus leaving the flight deck free most of the time to retrieve returning aircraft or launch missions. In actual operations, it quickly became clear that this was not practical. Storing ready aircraft in the hangar, anticipating that they would be moved up to the flight deck as needed and in the order needed, did not work. This was because the two small lifts on the 'Lexingtons' did not permit the rapid movement of aircraft between the hangar and flight deck, because the hangar was even smaller than the flight deck and surrounded by immovable bulkheads, making the movement of aircraft in the hangar far more difficult than on the flight deck, and because the lack of ventilation prevented the refuelling of aircraft in the hangar.

Having freed the hangar of the need to store the ready aircraft of the air group, there remained the need to find places to store spare aircraft. The reserve aircraft storage on the third deck, under the after deck of the hangar, provided room only for 'knocked down' aircraft that would take hours to assemble. What was needed was space to stow assembled aircraft that could quickly be substituted for wrecked or damaged machines. The air groups quickly looked to the ample overhead space in the 'Lexingtons'' hangars; unlike hangars in Royal Navy aircraft-carriers, those in US carriers were generally three decks high. By 1934 *Lexington* was experimenting with stowing aircraft in this space, hoisting nine spares or wrecks into the overhead with a jury-rigged system of tricing. This was found to allow aircraft to be satisfactorily stowed overhead and still left enough space below to carry on all normal hangar activities. By the next year *Lexington* felt confident enough to propose a more elaborate tricing arrangement that would allow twenty aircraft to be stowed, such that one could be hoisted in 30 minutes and lowered back to the hangar deck in 15 minutes.[1]

As the weight and size of aircraft increased, the manual system of hoisting and lowering triced aircraft became increasingly unworkable and it became harder to move aircraft on the hangar deck under stowed aircraft. Nevertheless, tricing had become an essential ingredient in aircraft handling on the 'Lexingtons'. In 1941 *Saratoga* reported that additional hoisting gear was being installed during her November refit:[2]

Left: Tricing, the hanging of spare or damaged aircraft from the hangar deckhead, freed up precious deck space in the hangar. This photo was taken by *Lexington*'s photographer in 1934 in support of a report on tricing experiments conducted in the ship. (NARA)

Below: The forward lift on the 'Lexingtons' was basically rectangular, but the ships had a pair of flaps that folded downwards over a hole in the flight deck that extended aft of the elevator platform. In theory, this allowed aircraft too big to fit on the platform to be lowered to the hangar, but this was rarely done and this photograph of *Saratoga* in February 1929 is rare in showing the flaps open. (NARA)

'We had tricing gear installed when we were in the yard in November and we used it a great deal. It made a difference. We could put 17 more airplanes on the ship. If you could trice up 17 of them, it was well worth taking a lot of inconvenience for.'[3]

The air department had no doubt about the value of tricing gear despite its occasional problems:

'Somebody said, in connection with the new carriers that there is a lot of discussion about the value of tricing equipment. I don't think it could be exaggerated. I don't give a damn if you can't pass planes under triced-up planes, there are times when you can use it and if you want to carry extra planes so you can have them triced up all the way aft - in the *Saratoga* type carrier you can trice them up all along one side. It's got to be good equipment, fast-working and then you can rotate planes and be very much more flexible.'[4]

Having these extra aircraft in the hangar did little good if there was no efficient way to move them to and from the flight deck. The most serious mistake made in the design of the 'Lexingtons' was the fitting of only two elevators; all subsequent US fleet aircraft-carriers had at least three elevators, with the sole exception of *Ranger* whose design was finalized before there had been much chance to benefit from experience with the 'Lexingtons'. Short of

Right: *Saratoga*'s hangar
deck was used for
ceremonial gatherings,
such as the ship's 17th
birthday celebrations on 16
November 1944. This photo
gives some idea of the
scale of this large open
space. Note the spare wing
stowage on the far
bulkhead. The gentleman in
the dark suit seated in the
middle of the centre section
was Joseph Grew, the last
pre-war US Ambassador to
Japan. (NARA)

Right: A Grumman Hellcat
being lowered to *Saratoga*'s
hangar while other fighters
warm up on the flight deck,
November 1943. It may
have been that this fighter
had engine trouble, in
which case lowering it on
the elevator would clear
the deck. (NARA)

adding another elevator to the 'Lexingtons',
which was never seriously considered due to
the relatively short hangar space in these ships,
the only other option was to enlarge and speed
up the existing pair. This work was identified as
one of the highest priority items in the 1938
'Circular of Requirements'. The plan at that time
was to replace the aft elevator with a larger one
and speed up the forward elevator, which
would also be given a larger platform. There

was lengthy debate over the specifications of
the new elevators. The new aft elevators, which
were to have been 44ft x 48ft, were ordered for
delivery on 1 January 1941, but the contractor
was already requesting delays in mid-1940.[5]
The forward elevator machinery was also
delayed and *Saratoga* went through both 1941
refits without change to her elevator gear;
Lexington went to her grave without change to
her elevators. In fact, the delays were such that

it would be late 1943 before practical plans were again being made to upgrade *Saratoga*'s elevators. At that time it was planned finally to install *Saratoga*'s new after elevator during her Hunters Point refit in January 1944.[6] In fact, even though the materials were finally available, the work was not done, because *Saratoga* had long since stopped using her aft elevator:

> 'Operational difficulties were such after the disappearance of folding wings that with the old equipment of the *Saratoga* we locked the after elevator in place and backed them down the ramp and planked over the after elevator well.'[7]

The planned enlargement and speeding up of the forward elevator continued to be discussed. In 1943 that elevator still was as originally installed, generally rectangular (59ft x 29ft) with partial-width hinged flaps in the flight deck aft of the elevator platform to accommodate the tails of aircraft too large to fit completely on the narrow platform. One plan for the new platform envisaged a T-shaped elevator, roughly the same size as the current one, with the platform extending aft to fill the hole made by the removal of the hinged flaps.[8] BuShips recommended that they simply adopt a lightweight elevator of the type being installed as original equipment in 'Essex'-class carriers of the same size (44ft x 48ft) as proposed for the aft elevator.[9] The new machinery speeding up the elevator was finally installed during *Saratoga*'s three-month yard visit to Puget Sound from June to August 1944.[10] On 9 March 1945 *Saratoga* officially requested that her now useless after elevator be removed to save weight and the hole in the flight deck patched up with deck plating.[11] This was done, and the new forward elevator platform was finally installed, during the yard visit following her Kamikaze damage in March 1945.[12]

Flight Deck

Because of the early decision not to use the hangar to store ready aircraft, the flight deck became the site of nearly all aviation-related activities. The fuelling and arming of aircraft (as described in Chapter 2) was done here; the arrester gear used to retrieve aircraft and later the catapults used to launch them were part of the flight deck structure.

The problem of retrieving aircraft on a short, narrow, pitching and rolling deck was the main obstacle to practical carrier aviation in its early days. In comparison, launching aircraft was

Above: Another use of the hangar was as a recreation space. While calisthenics and various ball games could be played on the flight deck, basketball requires a backboard, such as this one that could be lowered from the deckhead on *Saratoga*, 16 November 1944. (NARA)

relatively easy. The first arrester gear used by the British on HMS *Furious* was a rope net which, if the aircraft got that far, guaranteed major repairs.[13] The system used in the earliest experiments in the US Navy involved crossdeck ropes weighted with sandbags, a simple but rather impractical approach. When *Langley* was being converted, a reserve Lieutenant, Alfred 'Mel' Pride, was belatedly given the assignment of developing a practical arrester gear.[14] The system he developed was a variant of the then current RN system, the so-called 'Busteed Trap'.[15] The Busteed system used a pair of ramps and longitudinal wires. The aircraft, equipped with a row of small hooks extending downward from its landing gear, would roll up and over the first ramp, dropping into the 'trap' between the two ramps. The hooks, in theory at least, engaged the wires; the longitudinal wires kept the aircraft from veering to either side (aircraft brakes did not appear for another few years). The aircraft then rolled up the second ramp, and the friction of the hooks acting on the wires was supposed to stop the machine. Sometimes it did. Pride kept the longitudinal wires and small vertical hooks, to keep the

Above: The original
arrester gear on the
'Lexingtons' included
longitudinal wires held
above the deck by the
crossdeck rows of hinged
supports, known as fiddle
bridges. The aircraft
trapping on *Saratoga* on 26
January 1929 is a Vought
Corsair. Note the plane
guard destroyer in the
distance, a ship that
followed in the wake of an
aircraft-carrier to pick up
any pilots and aircrew who
missed the deck. (NARA)

plane straight, but discarded the ramps. Instead, he developed a tailhook and a set of lateral wires (pendants) to stop the aircraft. The drag necessary to do this was provided by gravity. Each wire was connected by pulley to a weight hanging from a tower; as the wire stretched out, the weight went up and the aircraft was slowed by the conversion of its kinetic energy into potential energy in the suspended weight. *Langley* was completed with the original Pride system with towers, but within a year the system had been redesigned to do

away with the towers, the weights hanging down into the hold.[16]

This system had the advantage of being self-contained, requiring no outside power source. It could keep working even if ship's power failed, but it was bulky, awkward and difficult to adjust for different weights of aircraft. Pride went off to continue his education and the Navy gave Carl Norden (inventor of the Norden bombsight) the job of designing the next generation of arrester gear. The 'Lexingtons' were completed with Norden's arresters, known as the Mk 1 gear.

Right: The longitudinal
wires worked, in theory, by
hooking the small anchors,
such as extend below the
undercarriage axle of this
Martin T4M torpedo-
bomber on *Lexington*, 4
April 1928. (NARA)

This gear retained the longitudinal wires as well as the crossdeck pendants, but there were those who thought the longitudinal wires were more of a hindrance than help:

> 'We should have discarded the fore-and-aft cables at the very beginning. We didn't discard them and they were put into the *Lexington* and *Saratoga*. It was there that a naval constructor named Stevens said, "Let's do away with those fore-and-aft cables." They were breaking up more aircraft than they were saving, but there was a great fear of going over the side.'[17]

In May 1929 *Saratoga* experimentally removed her longitudinal wires and discovered that there were fewer problems than with them.[18] The removal of these wires did reduce the rate of accidents but it also uncovered a latent problem with the Mk 1 arrester gear:

> 'Norden had designed this system which used a winch at each end of the crosswire. It was a winch that was hooked into the Waterbury speed gear that put pressure on a big brake. When I'd been on the *Lexington* for a while (I was on her for a couple of years), I was flight deck officer, and there was inherent difficulty with this gear. If a plane landed off center, it was inclined to go still further off center. In fact, it wanted to go over the side... Any deviation from the center was aggravated as the plane went up the deck.'[19]

The Mk 1 system had the added disadvantage of requiring an electric motor to return the gear to the ready position. Back from school, Pride was given the job of designing a better arrester. The resulting Mk 2 used hydraulics to stop the aircraft and return the gear to the ready position. This was authorized for installation in the 'Lexingtons' on 11 August 1931.[20]

The number and location of arrester pendants on the 'Lexingtons' was constantly changing. In 1934 four new Mk 3 units were installed, bringing the arrester layout to eight crossdeck pendants and four barriers.[21] The large number of pendants and barriers, especially compared with modern US aircraft-carriers which have just four pendants, was an attempt to prevent landing aircraft from missing all wires and barriers and crashing into the rest of the air group assembled forward. This number would only increase with the plan, first suggested in 1934, that the 'Lexingtons'' flight deck be widened forward, so that aircraft could be retrieved over the bow. To do this, it would be necessary to install a complete set of pendants and barriers forward.[22] After her flight deck was widened forward in 1936, *Lexington* had eight pendants forward in addition to the eight pendants and four barriers aft. These were by now a mix of Mk 3 and Mk 4 units. All the bow pendants were forward of the flight deck palisades. These were a set of hinged vertical strakes, located just forward of the forward elevator, designed to be raised to break up the flow of wind down the flight deck. (This was important only in the early days of naval aviation when aircraft were very light and could be lifted off the deck and damaged by a strong wind.) Some protection from the side was provided by life-netting extended along the side of the flight deck between the palisades and the aft 5in gun sponsons. Canvas strips were woven into this netting to block the wind. All edges of the flight deck which did not have some sort of deck-edge platform, such as a gun sponson, were provided with life netting for deck crewmen who might have to shelter from a runaway aircraft by diving over the edge of the deck. This netting folded upwards when flying operations were not in progress. By the

Above: A night Hellcat (note the radome on its right wing) traps on *Saratoga*, 2 February 1945. The arrester gear was now made up of a series of crossdeck pendants which caught the tailhook extending from the rear fuselage of the aircraft, and a series of two-wire barriers (two of which can be seen in this photo) to catch the aircraft if it missed the pendants. (NARA)

Right: The safety netting along the flight deck proved to be an excellent place to catch some sun for these airdales during a break in flying operations on *Saratoga*, November 1943. It was safe, comfortable and out of sight, three valuable features of any location for relaxation. (NARA)

Above: A Grumman TBM Avenger takes off from *Saratoga* at the time of the last Rabaul raids, 5 November 1943. Note the flaps covering the holes where the forward pendants were led below deck to the hydraulic pistons that actually slowed the aircraft. At this point, the pendants have been removed but the below-deck mechanisms, and these flaps, remain. (NARA)

time the widened flight deck was added to *Saratoga*, one additional pendant and three forward barriers had been added to the set-up. (It was considered bad form to catch a 'late wire', qualifying one to be labelled a 'Dilbert'. An analysis of the landings on *Lexington* in FY37 showed that on *Lexington* 33.1 per cent caught the first wire and 97.3 per cent caught one of the first four.)[23]

The forward arrester gear was installed simply to allow aircraft to be recovered over the bow if the aft flight deck was damaged. All pre-war US aircraft-carriers were given this feature, except for *Langley*, despite the fact that only the 'Lexingtons' had the turbo-electric drive which

allowed them to go as fast astern as forward. However, in actual operations, this feature was rarely if ever used.[24] In July 1943 OpNav made a blanket recommendation that all forward arrester gear on all aircraft-carriers be removed.[25] As far as can be told from photographic evidence, the crew of *Saratoga* went ahead and removed the forward pendants, but not the hydraulic units, while at sea in late 1943. The actual removal of all the forward mechanical components was done at Puget Sound during the yard period ending August 1944.[26]

The 'Lexingtons' were completed with a single flywheel catapult. It was there solely to permit the launching of seaplanes; wheeled aircraft of the time had no need of a catapult to get airborne. In fact, seaplanes were hardly ever carried in the 'Lexingtons' and the catapult went unused. The inspectors in 1931 reported:

'The catapult is seldom used. The record book shows that dead loads have been fired from it five times during the commissioning of the ship, the last shot being made in August 1928.'[27]

It is not too surprising, therefore, that authority to remove the catapult came in 1932, although nothing official was done about it until 1936.[28] By 1938 plans were being made to install two new steam catapults in the forward flight deck of *Lexington* (and of *Saratoga* when her flight deck was widened).[29] Still, nothing was done since aircraft still seemed fully capable of launching under nearly all circumstances without the aid of a catapult. However, as aircraft continued to get larger and heavier, it was inevitable that catapults would be needed at some point. That point came in June 1944 when *Saratoga* was taken in hand for conversion to a night duty carrier. At that time she was given a pair of Type H Mk 2 Mod 1 catapults, which she retained until the end of the war.[30]

Aircraft Handling

In peacetime each squadron of aircraft was an independent entity. Squadrons were organized on a more or less permanent basis into air groups, led by the Commander, Air Group (CAG). Air groups were more or less permanently assigned to aircraft-carriers, although they could be given shore duty for extended periods. Each squadron was a free-standing unit, complete not only with aircraft and pilots, but with maintenance personnel and spare parts inventories as well. So when a squadron was assigned shore duty, even temporarily, it took not only aircraft ashore, but also all its support staff and their impedimenta.[31] Even if a squadron was to be ashore only for the few days its carrier was in port, it would need its complete staff if it intended to do any flying before the ship sailed again. Once the war started, this habit was quickly broken.

The movement of aircraft on and near the aircraft-carrier was the responsibility of the ship's air department, led by the air officer. Air department personnel moved aircraft around the flight deck, armed and fuelled them, unhooked them from arrester wires and hooked them into the catapults; they comprised the five 'V' divisions of the ship's company. Air department personnel also planned air strikes, plotted the movement of aircraft in the air around the ship and directed fighter defence of the ship.

The direction of an aircraft-carrier's defence in the air was the job of the fighter direction officer (FDO). From his position in air plot (later the CIC), he gathered all available data concerning the numbers and location of enemy aircraft, and the numbers and location of his own combat air patrol (CAP), and used those data to direct his fighters to points in the sky that would, in theory, allow them to intercept the enemy. The data came from any available source. In the days before radar, it would come from lookouts in the tops, from airborne scouts and CAP aircraft and from other ships. The FDO would try to keep a clear picture of the situation on a grease board in air plot. Later, with the advent of radar and IFFs, the picture got both clearer and more confusing, since the field of action was now much larger and the amount of information available was often overwhelming.

FDO procedures at the beginning of the war were primitive. Even if radar did give the fighter

Left: During 1944 the safety netting along *Saratoga*'s flight deck was replaced largely by catwalks such as this, forward on the starboard side. This was more practical but a far less comfortable place to lounge around. Note the avgas control station in the foreground. (NARA)

Below left: Aircrew get their assignments in a pre-mission briefing in one of *Saratoga*'s ready rooms, November 1943. There was one large ready room built into the 'Lexingtons' in the island at flight deck level, but this proved inadequate in combat and a second larger one was carved out of wardroom officer's country on the main deck. (NARA)

Below: Based on experience with *Langley*, the 'Lexingtons' had an LSO helping pilots trap almost from the beginning. *Lexington*'s LSO uses flags to help this amphibian aboard in March 1929. The flags, which could be hard to see as they fluttered in the crossdeck breeze, were soon replaced by paddles. (NARA)

director a relatively clear picture of the airborne environment, it did not distinguish friends from enemies, and many wasted sorties were spent intercepting a returning scout. The only solution, until IFF came along later in the war, was for returning aircraft to break radio silence and announce their presence. The radar picture available to the FDO at this stage of the war showed bearing only, not altitude. These shortcomings led to some instances when the CAP failed to adequately protect a carrier and to complaints from pilots:

> 'I think the subject of fighter direction hasn't been given high enough priority in the Fleet. The facilities are not what they should be. If the ability of our fighter pilots, the communications facilities and the fighter direction system were exploited to the fullest extent we could annihilate an enemy carrier attack group before they dropped their bombs or torpedoes.'[32]

Later, *Saratoga*'s FDO moved with the radar sets themselves into the new combat information centre (CIC) established in the aft half of the captain's cabin on the main deck. There he had the advantage of more and better radars, many equipped with IFF systems, but this was still not enough. In the afternoon and evening of 21 February 1945, *Saratoga* was attacked by at least ten enemy aircraft in two waves. A four-plane CAP was aloft and fourteen more fighters were launched in the last minutes before the first attack but only one of the two CAP sections

made contact with the incoming attackers and accounted for, at best, two of the enemy. The CAP's failure adequately to defend the ship was the result of a number of factors. *Saratoga* complained about the relatively short range of the IFF. Even though the incoming raid was picked up at 75nm, at that range there was no indication of hostility and, in any case, the relative unreliability of IFF made such identifications doubtful. What made the situation worse on this occasion was that, after broadcasting the contact to the rest of the Iwo Jima Air Support Group, the commander of that group evaluated the contact as 'returning itinerant friendlies'. It was not until the attackers split into two groups to approach *Saratoga* from different sides, seven minutes after the initial detection, that the contact was identified as probably hostile and action was taken to intercept.[33]

The job of guiding aircraft to a safe 'trap' was the responsibility of the landing signals officer (LSO):

> 'The business of using arm signals to show whether the pilot was high or low or fast or slow came about in an interesting way...The executive officer [of *Langley*] was Commander Kenneth Whiting, who had been largely responsible for our having a carrier. He was in the netting, just below the flight deck level where the personnel go while aircraft are landing. He used to stand in the netting all the way aft on the port side. That was a good place to see what's going on.

'We had one pilot who had not landed on the deck before, but had had a lot of training and practice ashore....

'This chap came in, and apparently he was very reluctant to actually set his plane down. He kept on coming in high, and then he'd give her the gun before he quite got to the deck, and go around again. This had happened several times. Whiting jumped up on the deck and grabbed the white hats from two bluejackets who were there, and he held them up to indicate that this character was too high. Then he put them down. He coached the fellow in, and that seemed like a good idea.

'So from then on, an officer was stationed aft there with flags to signal whether the plane was high or low or coming in too fast or too slow.'[34]

The LSO very quickly became a permanent feature of the landing operation. He was given his own platform at the port aft corner of the flight deck, and later a second one at the starboard bow corner of the flight deck when it was widened forward.

When *Saratoga* had her flight deck extended aft in 1941, apparently her LSO's platform was not relocated because, in October 1942, she was complaining that the LSO could not see the ramp from his position and as a result was waving planes down too early, particularly during night operations. As a result, the platform was relocated aft during the repair period following *Saratoga*'s second torpedoing.[35] The final revision to the LSO's platform on *Saratoga* came in 1945, when it was given a power-operated windscreen, since the same desirable wind across the deck that allowed aircraft to land more slowly also buffeted the LSO.[36]

The flight deck officer (who was also the V-1 division officer) had the job of organizing the movement of aircraft around the flight deck. Even today this is a formidable challenge, but in the days before angled decks it was thankless. No matter where aircraft are pushed, they are bound to be in the way of some other activity. The spotting of aircraft was a minor art; aircraft had to be pushed forward to make room aft to retrieve a mission, then pushed aft to make room forward to launch the next. Aircraft that needed refuelling had to be pushed forward, because the avgas piping ran up to the forward end of the flight deck (Fly I). Rearmament was done mainly in the mid-deck region (Fly II), where the bomb and torpedo elevators reached the flight deck, but munitions could be wheeled to the aircraft if necessary. When all this was completed, then the aircraft were respotted aft in anticipation of the next launch.

Not only was it critical where aircraft were spotted but in what order, because different types of machine might need to be launched first (such as fighters or scouts), so they were spotted closest to the bow, while others might need the longest take-off roll (such as torpedo bombers) and they would be placed furthest to the rear. A sailor reported on the very early days of flying operations on *Lexington*:

'Scouts were launched first, followed by fighters and then the torpedo planes. Spotting of the planes was plotted in the ready room using a model flight deck and scale-model metal planes (flat pieces). Every time a different type of plane was put into service it changed the parking picture due to different length, wing span, etc. Allowance had to be made for propeller clearance of the plane ahead. Once in a while wheel chocks would shift and a prop would chew up a rudder. This would put a plane or two out of service, cause the use of bad language, the writing of reports which had to be read by numerous people who took their rank and supposed importance seriously. Then someone got chewed out right down the line to the Sea2c who had not noticed that the chocks had slipped.'[37]

Aircraft movement on the flight deck was controlled by various means. The 1931 inspection noted that the air officer had an observation position in the bridge structure overlooking the flight deck. Sometime within the next few years, the air officer found a more permanent perch in the aerological platform (the second level of the island structure originally known as the meteorological platform). There the air department set up the air plot and air intelligence offices. The air officer was given a small platform of his own extending out over the flight deck with a large blackboard on which he wrote a description of the next operation for the information of flight deck crew and pilots. A 1934 BuAer memo cited the successful installation of a flight deck loudspeaker system on *Ranger* and recommended its installation on the Navy's other aircraft-carriers. At the same time, the bureau recommended that a better visual means be found to communicate with pilots than the air officer's blackboard.[38] This was never done and photos of *Saratoga* at war show the same blackboard in use to communicate with the flight deck.

During the reconstruction of *Saratoga*'s island in early 1942, two major changes were made to ease control of air operations and communication of flight data to the aircrews. To

Left: This Hellcat flipped
over and caught fire after
catching a barrier on
Saratoga, 12 December
1944. The fire is almost out
and crewmen gather
around the aircraft trying to
get to the pilot. When a
machine ended up on its
back, like this, the pilot
could easily get trapped in
the wreck. In this case, the
new forklift truck, on the
right, came to the rescue,
lifting the wreck so that the
pilot could be freed. That
and fast work putting out the
fire saved the pilot's life. He
escaped with minor injuries;
fatalities were rare. (NARA)

Right: The flag bridge
level is lined with staff
officers observing flying
operations on *Saratoga*,
November 1943. The flight
deck control officer, with his
talker in the Pri-Fly on the
wing of the navigation
bridge, took a much more
professional interest in the
goings on. He has several
means of communicating
with the flight deck,
including the traffic lights at
the lower left in this view.
(NARA)

Right: The air officer had a
catwalk outside the air
department offices on the
aerologic level of the island
from which he could
observe flight deck activity
on *Saratoga*, November
1943. Note the blackboard
on the island bulkhead that
told the deck crew the
particulars of the next
operation. (NARA)

facilitate the latter, a box-like structure with two
racks, each with room for four large number
placards, was built into the outer face of the
secondary flight control position on the sky aft
platform. The top row of numerals gave the
target's bearing and the second row could give
the distance or altitude of the target:

> 'When operating in an area where contacts
> with hostile scouting and reconnaissance
> aircraft are to be expected and radio silence is
> in effect, it is considered most desirable to
> keep the combat air patrol close to the
> controlling ship and at low altitude. When
> "bogies" were picked up on the radar screen
> it has been *Saratoga* practice to post at Fly II
> large numerals indicating the bearing, distance
> and, when available, the altitude of the
> unidentified planes. By prearranged
> searchlight signal the CAP was recalled, flew
> close aboard, acquired the necessary
> information and proceeded on the
> investigation with a minimum of delay.'[39]

To control the actual launch of aircraft, a flight
deck officer was given a corner of the bridge
wing at the navigation bridge level where he
could see the length of the flight deck and
control the take-off of individual aircraft by
means of an aft-facing traffic light.

1. BuCon, Lex -> BuCon, 20 May 1935, Hangar Overhead
   Airplane Hoisting Sheaves; Installation of; *Lexington*
   Alteration Request No. 50-35.
2. I&S, Report of Material Inspection of U.S.S. *Saratoga* (CV3)
   Held November 4-6, 1941.
3. BuShips, 16 June 1942, Interview of Commander Alfred M.
   Pride in the Bureau of Aeronautics, p 10.
4. BuShips, 4 June 1942, Interview Commander C.R. Brown,
   Air Officer, U.S.S. *Saratoga* in Bureau of Aeronautics, p 8.
5. BuShips, NYPS -> BuShips, 16 September 1940, USS
   Saratoga (CV3) – Modernization – Commencement of
   First Period.
6. BuShips, NYPS -> NYPS, 6 November 1943, USS *Saratoga* -
   Installation of Airplane Elevator Aft – Modification of Flight
   Deck and Main Deck Plating.
7. BuShips, 4 June 1942, Interview Commander C.R. Brown,
   Air Officer, U.S.S. *Saratoga* in the Bureau of Aeronautics,
   p 8. Commander Brown was referring to the introduction
   of the non-folding wing SBDs and F4Fs in 1941, but the
   problem did not disappear when they were replaced by
   still larger aircraft with folding wings.
8. BuShips, BuAer -> BuShips, 29 December 1943, USS
   Saratoga (CV3) – Forward Elevator, Modification of.
9. BuShips, NYPS -> BuShips, 11 February 1944, U.S.S.
   Saratoga (CV3) – Forward Elevator - Modifications to.
10. BuShips, , 8 August 1944, NYPS Departure Report, p 7.
11. BuShips, Sara -> BuShips, 9 March 1945, U.S.S.*Saratoga*
    (CV3) – Alteration Request No. 34-45, Removal of after
    elevator platform.
12. BuShips, 14 May 1945, NYPS Departure Report, p 23-4.
13. GenBd, CinCUS -> SecNav, 15 November 1918, Report
    on Development of Air Service in British Grand Fleet.
14. This was the same A.M. Pride who, as a Commander,
    served as *Saratoga*'s XO in 1941-2.

15. Oral, Pride Interview No.1, p 30. Also known as the 'Harp' or 'B-Gear'.
16. ibid, p 34.
17. ibid, p 31. The constructor was Lieutenant Commander Leslie Stevens.
18. BuCon, Sara -> ComAirBatFor, 11 May 1929, USS *Saratoga* (CV3) Arresting Gear – Experimental landings without Longitudinal Wires.
19. op.cit, p 35-6.
20. I&S, , 4 November 1931, Report of Material Inspection of U.S.S. *Lexington* (CV2) Held 27, 28 and 29 October 1931, p 76-7.
21. The first barrier was a hybrid unit including a crossdeck pendant, so some sources report nine wires and three barriers or even nine wires and four barriers.
22. BuCon, CinCUS -> BuCon, 15 Oct 1934, U.S.S. *Saratoga* and U.S.S. *Lexington* – Alteration to Flight Deck at Bow (Second Endorsement).
23. GenBd, BuAer -> CNO, 18 September 1937, Analysis of Aircraft-carrier Operations - Fiscal Year 1937. In fairness to *Saratoga*'s air group, it should be noted that *Lexington*'s first four wires were spread further apart than *Saratoga*'s.
24. The author has found no instance of aircraft being retrieved over the bow and only one example of aircraft being launched astern. That took place on 7 December 1941, when *Lexington* was steaming towards Midway with a deckload of Marine SB2Us forward. In order to launch a relief CAP without respotting the SB2Us, the F2As of VF-2 were spotted aft of the scout bombers and launched over the stern.
25. GenBd, VCNO -> BuShips, 22 July 1943, Aircraft-carriers -Bow Arresting Gear. No reason was given in this letter, but undoubtedly it was due to the fact that aircraft-carriers now never operated alone and that, should one flight deck get damaged, others were available to recover airborne aircraft.
26. BuShips, , 8 August 1944, NYPS Departure Report, p 15-6.
27. I&S, , 4 November 1931, Report of Material Inspection of U.S.S. *Lexington* (CV2) Held 27, 28 and 29 October 1931, p 145.
28. BuCon, Sara -> BuCon, 16 August 1936, Removal of catapult machinery and tracks. The authority was granted in an order dated 21 May 1932 referenced in this document
29. BuCon, BuAer -> NYPS, 26 September 1938, U.S.S. *Lexington* (CV2) and U.S.S. *Saratoga* (CV3) – Modernization of.
30. BuShips, , 8 August 1944, NYPS Departure Report, p 15.
31. This organization was due in part to the fact that most aircraft in the early days of aviation were produced in very small numbers, often only enough to equip a squadron or two, and a replacement squadron stood a good chance of flying a different type of aircraft.
32. BuShips, , 26 August 1942, Interview of Lt. Cdr. John S. Thach in the Bureau of Aeronautics.
33. BuShips, Sara -> CinCUS, 26 February 1945, U.S.S. *Saratoga* (CV3) Action Report for the period 0900 (K) to 2130 (K), 21 February 1945.
34. Oral, Pride Interview No. 2, p 61-3.
35. BuShips, Fleet Maintenance Officer -> BuShips, 12 Oct 1942, U.S.S. *Saratoga* (CV3) - Landing Signal Platform - Relocation of.
36. BuShips, , 14 May 1945, NYPS Departure Report.
37. Schwartz, Max R., Lady Lex – The Early Days, in The Hook, Fall 1981.
38. BuCon, BuAer -> BuEng, 29 Oct 1934, Sound Survey on Flight Deck of USS *Saratoga*.
39. BuShips, Sara -> CinCPac, 19 August 1942, Report of Action Tulagi - Guadalcanal Offensive 7-8 August, 1942.

Left: Looking up from the forward lift platform, it is possible to see most of the air control facilities on *Saratoga*, including the air officer's blackboard and Pri-Fly on the bridge wing just above the conning tower. The aerial projecting from the side of Sky Forward was for the short-range TBS, November 1943. (NARA)

Left: One way of communicating with the CAP when radio silence was in force was by means of the large numbers hanging from the side of the secondary flight control station in Sky Aft. This photo was taken on *Saratoga*, 31 October 1943. The numbers gave the bearing and altitude of the likely target. (NARA)

5. Radio and Radar

This chapter covers the radio and radar systems used by the 'Lexingtons' to warn of enemy activity, to identify threats and to communicate with friendly aircraft and ships. In the approximately 40 years of the 'Lexingtons'' careers, these systems evolved rapidly, extending the distance at which they could see and communicate and the conditions under which such vision or communication was possible. By the end of the Second World War, night and bad weather had not only ceased to be a major obstacle, but had indeed become the very conditions under which *Saratoga* was expected to operate. Throughout their careers, the 'Lexingtons'' own air groups represented the longest-ranging detection system available. In enemy waters, defensive patrols were mounted constantly, particularly against enemy submarines, and offensive scouting missions were the necessary first stage in naval warfare. With carrier groups able to strike at enemies 200 or more miles away, the critical advantage in battle fell to the side that could find the enemy's fleet first and put its striking power out of action.[1]

5.1 Radio

Radio was well known prior to the First World War, but it had surprisingly little impact on the conduct of that war at sea or in the air. It was too unreliable to affect the naval war significantly and the apparatus was too big and heavy to put in aircraft. Nevertheless, there could be no doubt in the world's navies that both these problems would be resolved in the coming years. By the time the 'Lexingtons' were launched, they were equipped with a comprehensive outfit of radios designed to serve a number of different functions.

The 'Lexingtons'' original radio outfit was distributed by function to various locations around the ships. Radio I (or main radio), located at the aft end of the communications platform level of the island, held the ships' primary receivers. Radio II (or main transmitting) was located at flight deck level in the funnel structure, sandwiched between the aftermost uptake and the ammunition handling room for No. 3 main battery turret. As the name suggests, this compartment held the ships' primary transmitting equipment. Radio III (or emergency radio) was located on the main deck at Frame 10 on the far starboard side and contained the back-up radio equipment to be employed in case any or all of the three other sites in the superstructure were damaged. Radio IV (or Air Radio), located on the aerological platform level of the island, contained those radio sets specifically dedicated to communication with the ships' air groups. A complete inventory of *Lexington*'s radio equipment made in 1940 showed the following (one of each except where noted):

In Radio I:
    RAA, receiver (3 units)
    RAB, receiver (2 units)
    RAB-2a, receiver (3 units)
    RAB-3, receiver
    RAK-2, receiver
    RAL-2, receiver
In Radio II:
    TAQ, transmitter
    TBM-3, transmitter
    TBF, transmitter
    TBA, transmitter
    TBH, transmitter
    TAT-1, transmitter
    TAK, transmitter
    RO-2a, receiver
In Radio III:
    TU-3, transmitter

Below: Radios all looked the same; they were black boxes with an array of dials and meters in the front. This photo shows the RAK and RAL receivers on the shelf in Radio I together with an assortment of switchboxes and speakers, *Saratoga*, 21 July 1946. (NARA)

TBH, transmitter
TAT-1, transmitter
TBK-3, transmitter
RO, receiver
In air plot:
RAA, receiver
RAB-3, receiver
In flag radio:
RAB, receiver[2]

The two RO receivers (in Radio II and Radio III) were considered obsolete and were in the process of being replaced by RAK-4 or RAL-4 sets.

The last major change in the radio suite before the war was the introduction of the YE aircraft homing beacon (intended to work in conjunction with a ZB homing adaptor added to the standard RU-4 receiver on the aircraft), which was added to *Lexington* in March 1941[3] and to *Saratoga* sometime before November of that year.[4] The YE was originally housed in its own radio room on the flag bridge level. The prominent YE aerial was mounted on the foretop.

The same fate befell the 'Lexingtons'' radio equipment as most of their other systems; many schemes were put forward during the late 1930s to upgrade the ships' radios, but no major changes were actually made. On 15 January 1942 *Lexington* complained about the age and unreliability of her receivers:

> 'It is urgently requested that all or any of the eight type RAB Radio receivers now installed in this ship be replaced as soon as possible. These sets are worn out, unreliable and beyond the capacity of the ship's force to keep in repair...
>
> 'There is at least one receiver out of commission for repairs each day...
>
> 'Even though the standard of maintenance, up-keep, and checking has been high, the general deterioration has reached an extremely advanced stage. The majority of failures are due to burned-out resistors and defective by-pass condensers (sic)...
>
> 'Attempts have been made to alleviate this situation on the voice radio circuits by obtaining commercial type receivers, but as yet none have been available. Two such sets now in use by the flag are more satisfactory and more reliable than the ship's receivers.'[5]

A completely new type of radio was fitted to *Saratoga* during her refit in early 1942. All her previous radios had been designed to work in the medium- and high-frequency (MF and HF) ranges. The crystals reported by *Lexington* in

her 1940 inspection ranged from 175kHz to 3,153kHz (3.153MHz) in the MF and HF bands.[6] MF and HF equipment was far easier to design and maintain than higher-frequency radios, but had the disadvantage of generating radio signals that bounced off the ionosphere and could be intercepted by listeners well beyond the horizon. To prevent radio signals from being reflected by the ionosphere, a higher frequency was needed.[7] Realizing the need for a radio that would allow ships in a task force to communicate without fear of being overheard, the Navy developed the TBS (Talk Between Ships) system in the VHF band (72.5MHz). *Saratoga* was fitted with a TBS-2 set in Radio I. At the same time, the TAT-1 in Radio II was replaced by a TBU set and the same change was made in Radio III, where a TAJ-8 set was added as well.[8]

TBS sets had been available in destroyers for some time before the war, but were only installed in major fleet units such as *Saratoga* as a result of bitter experience. Had *Saratoga* had a

Above: This view of *Saratoga* entering Espiritu Santo on 16 May 1944 shows the inboard outrigger carrying radio aerials around the aft end of the funnel. (NARA)

TBS before she was torpedoed the first time, she might just have avoided the damage. Commander 'Mel' Pride, then *Saratoga*'s XO, recalled reaching the bridge four minutes after the torpedo struck:

> 'As I came on the signal bridge, I noticed a destroyer on our port bow blinking. I inquired what the signal was and they said, "They're just telling us that two torpedoes have just gone by them headed for the *Saratoga*". (The point that I wish to make is that the communications from the screen to the *Saratoga* were most inadequate to cover the situation. We had no warning whatsoever - nobody saw the tracks; there was no warning that the ship was to be torpedoed.) As I recall it, that particular destroyer was out close to 5,000 yards and we probably would have been able to swing the ship one way or the other if we'd had warning. That situation has been cleared up now by the installation of bridge radio. The little talky-talky set which the destroyers have had some time has now been

installed in the large ships also...If we had had it that night I think it might possibly have averted the hit.'[9]

Additional VHF equipment was installed in *Saratoga* as the war progressed. An RBK receiver was installed in air radio in 1943, where it was found to be effective at a range of 130nm at a frequency of 142MHz. However, its effectiveness was significantly reduced due to interference from the CXAM-1 radar carried on the forward lip of the funnel.[10]

The creation of two CIC spaces on *Saratoga*'s main deck during the Hunters Point refit in early 1944 allowed the installation of a number of additional radios. At least four RBH receivers were installed in the main CIC and a TBS-3 set was installed in the auxiliary CIC. A YG low-power radio beacon was installed on her mainmast at the same time.[11] During her Puget Sound refit in the summer of that year, further incremental upgrades of her radio outfit were

Below: Standard wire aerials were gradually replaced by whip aerials as *Saratoga* was successively modernized. This view on 10 September 1945 shows one such aerial right by Radio II at the base of the funnel aft. Note the 40mm guntubs outboard of the funnel. (NARA)

made. Specifically, one TBK-9, TBA, TBU and TAQ were removed from Radio II and replaced by TAJ and TDE transmitter sets. The TBS set in Radio I was replaced by two more powerful sets and an RBO and RAU set were also installed. The TBS-3 set installed in the auxiliary CIC was moved to Radio II. At the same time, the four RBH receivers in the main CIC were replaced by RBS units. The RAS receiver in the aerology office was removed and replaced by RAO and RBL sets.[12]

As *Saratoga* was being prepared for duty as a night carrier, she was given several extra pieces of radio equipment needed to guide aircraft in the dark. These included a third homing beacon, a YJ-1, installed on a foundation projecting from the foremast on either side of the forward SG aerial, a CPN-6 beacon installed lower down on the same mast, and a pair of 2AX-NAN infra-red beacons mounted one on each side of the SK platform on the foretop.[13]

The positioning of the aerials for these radios was to be a constant problem, not solved until fairly late in the ships' careers. The aerials for sets located in Radio I or air radio caused the least problem, as these were run up from the island to the foremast yardarm or the funnel and were thus out of the way of most activities. Aerials serving the transmitters in Radio II posed more of a problem as they were carried up the aft end of the funnel and around the funnel structure by an outrigger that projected over the flight deck. At least one early accident was caused when an aircraft came in high and caught its wing on the outrigger.[14] The more serious problem was the location of the aerials from Radio III, which emerged from the hull near the starboard forward 5in gun sponson. The only way they could be erected was by means of a temporary mast which had to be lowered in combat because it interfered with flying operations and all forward guns. This problem was only solved with the introduction of whip aerials during the course of the war. These were quarter-wave, free-standing rigid aerials that were mounted vertically with one end grounded to the ship's structure; they rapidly replaced long single-wire aerials. Late-war photographs of *Saratoga* show numerous whips projecting upwards from the island and funnel. They were most handy, however, for Radio III, where three whips were mounted from the starboard forward 40mm sponsons and one from the port side. They were hinged so that they could be set vertically for best radio operation and easily lowered to the horizontal to get them out of the way of flying operations.

1. A major difference in US and Japanese doctrine in the Second World War was the Japanese reliance on seaplanes to perform scouting as opposed to the American use of the hybrid scout-bomber, such as the SBD. Part of the blame for the Japanese defeat at Midway must fall to the delay in launching the seaplane scout assigned to the sector in which the US fleet was located.
2. BuShips, NYPS -> BuShips, 11 September 1940, Radio – U.S.S. *Lexington* – Inspection of Radio, Underwater Sound and Electric Visual Signalling Installations, Report of.
3. BuShips, Lex -> BuShips, 11 March 1941, Naval Message 112052.
4. I&S, Report of Material Inspection of U.S.S. *Saratoga* (CV3) Held November 4-6, 1941.

5. BuShips, Lex -> BuShips, 15 January 1942, Radio receivers - Replacement of.
6. BuShips, NYPS -> BuShips, 11 September 1940, Radio – U.S.S. *Lexington* – Inspection of Radio, Underwater Sound and Electric Visual Signalling Installations, Report of.
7. As long as it was not too high. MF/HF waves, up to 30MHz, are reflected by the ionosphere; UHF waves, above 300MHz, are reflected by the troposphere. VHF waves, between the two reflecting bands, pass through the atmosphere without reflection.
8. BuShips, NYPS -> BuShips, 2 June 1942, U.S.S. *Saratoga* - Inspection of Radio, Underwater Sound equipment - Departure Inspection – Report of.
9. BuShips, , 16 June 1942, Interview of Commander Alfred M. Pride in the Bureau of Aeronautics, p 4.
10. BuShips, Sara -> BuShips, 26 October 1943, Radar Interference with Radio Communication Equipment.
11. BuShips, Sara -> BuShips, 20 March 1945, Naval Message 192309. In this message, *Saratoga* complained that the YG had an effective range of only 8 miles.
12. BuShips, 8 September 1944, NYPS Departure Report.
13. BuShips, 10 January 1945, NYPH Departure Report.
14. BuCon, 13 December 1929, Aircraft Trouble Report.

5.2 Radar

The 'Lexingtons' carried a variety of radars, from the first crude, limited production variants to the more sophisticated equipment in use by the end of the war. This progression tended to be in discrete stages, with major upgrades coming at almost every yard period. Radars quickly became categorized as to type. Thus, there were search radars (further subdivided into air search and surface search) and fire control radars. At each upgrade, radars of a type tended to be replaced by newer equipment of the same type. This section covers the evolution of the 'Lexingtons'' radar suite chronologically, describing the improvement and proliferation of each type of radar system at each of the progressive stages.

Note on US radar designations: The US used multiple designation systems; BuOrd, which had responsibility for fire control radars, used a one-up mark system (starting with Mk 1), while BuShips, which had responsibility for search radars, used a letter system. In this system, the prefix letter(s) designated type and the suffix letter(s) designated sequence (starting with 'A'). Common prefixes were 'F' for fire control, 'S' for search, 'X' for experimental and 'CX' for commercial experimental (i.e., developed by a contractor, such as RCA, rather than a government laboratory, such as NRL). To confuse matters, BuShips gave its own designations to BuOrd radars. Thus the fourth fire control radar, the Mk 4, was also known as the FD. These designations applied only to the Navy; if the Army used the same radar, it would have yet another designation. Finally, late in the

war, an inter-service system came into effect that used a three-letter prefix and a one-up number suffix. This saw little if any use for radars during the war but was used for other electronics. Thus the SPR-1 and SPT-4 RCM gear described in the next section.

1941

The 'Lexingtons' received the US Navy's first limited production radar, the CXAM-1.[1] It had a large mattress aerial mounted on a small platform erected on the forward lip of the funnel. The control room for the radar was a new structure built on the forward edge of the funnel immediately below the aerial platform, replacing the Pri-Fly and secondary conning station previously located there. The radar display, a Type A oscilloscope, was sited in the air plot on the aerological platform, making an already crowded space even more so. *Saratoga's* was mounted during her first 1941 Puget Sound refit[2]; *Lexington's* was added in June at Pearl Harbor following the plans already drawn up for *Saratoga*.[3] However, radar was still in its infancy and both ships complained of the unreliability of the equipment. *Saratoga* reported:

> 'It was very unreliable. The darn thing would catch aircraft one day and not catch surface craft, and then they'd do some tinkering with it and it would catch surface craft this side of the horizon but would not catch any airplanes. And you couldn't know whether it was working or not. To give an instance: On the first of December we left Puget Sound and headed south. We ran at 27 knots from Tatoosh south in heavy fog. I expressed a little doubt about the procedure, and the captain said that he thought the radar would give us ample warning of any possible collision. So we churned along, the radar showing the usual line on the screen. And against all probability 24 hours later it still had shown nothing. Well, you know very well, it is difficult to conceive going down from Tatoosh to the Farallones without meeting anything. However, just after dark we sighted the lights of San Francisco lightship and as we drew near I went up to see what it would show on the radar screen and it didn't show a darn thing. And we had steamed all that time at high speed thinking we had radar protection.'[4]

An RCA service technician met the ship at Pearl Harbor, repaired the broken parts, as well as some others discovered to be malfunctioning, and adjusted the radio frequency (RF) to 186MHz (c1.6m).[5] *Lexington* took a technician with her when she sailed for a few days' gunnery practice in late October 1941. On the first day, the CXAM lost all sensitivity after the firing of the fifth main battery salvo, the cause diagnosed as the jarring loose of tubes and solder connections; the fault occurred again the next day, the transmitter failing because power leads shook loose. The vibration also induced cracks and short-circuits in oscillator valves. The repairman got the radar working again after one hour on the first day and after two hours on the second.[6] When the CXAM was working, it provided excellent search capability. It could detect a single aircraft at 80nm at high altitude, at 35nm at 3,000ft and at 20nm (40,000yd) at low altitude. An aircraft-carrier, cruiser and destroyer could be detected at 30,000, 26,000 and 18,000yd, respectively.[7]

Saratoga had two FC (Mk 3) main battery fire control radars added, one during and one immediately after her November 1941 refit.[8] Their aerials were mounted on the fore and aft 5in control tops, directly connected one level down to the 8in directors, so that it was necessary to turn the director to turn the aerial.[9] The FC was a significant technological advance over the CXAM in both capability and reliability. It operated at a much shorter wavelength (40cm), giving significantly better resolution, and introduced lobe switching, a process by which bearing was refined by switching the signal alternately between two horizontal halves of the aerial and comparing the returns until they were approximately equal. The after

installation apparently caused no problems, but the forward aerial was positioned behind the 5in directors, which caused significant interference. Plans for enlarging the foretop to allow the directors to be moved were considered, but this was not done during the November refit and events would soon render it unnecessary.[10]

A routine was quickly established for using the new radar, which was employed not only for fire control but as a back-up search set. The sets were switched off during daylight and good visibility, but at GO at night and in poor visibility the set was kept on and used to sweep the horizon every 15 minutes, looking for formation changes or any new echoes. The aerial was aimed at the horizon and could not be elevated, but it proved effective against single low-flying aircraft at 3,500yd and formations of aircraft at 10-12,000yd. The radar could at any time be diverted back to its original purpose, fire control for the main battery.[11] In a fire control role, accuracy of 50yd at a range of 23,000yd on a heavy cruiser and a range of 18,000yd on a destroyer were reported.[12] *Saratoga* was very pleased with her new acquisition:

'The two FC radar sets, installed recently at the Navy Yard and under way, have proved satisfactory in the short time they have been operating, and are considered among the most valuable equipment aboard for fighting the ship. There are frequent minor breakdowns, probably to be expected on any new design of high-frequency apparatus. In the three weeks

Below: *Lexington* received a CXAM-1 radar, probably in June 1941, during a refit at Pearl Harbor. This view from the apron on Ford Island was taken soon after that. The CXAM aerial is just visible at the forward lip of the funnel. Note the radar room about midway down the forward edge of the funnel structure and the funnel cap on the forward uptake. (NARA)

of experience with it, ship's personnel have now become sufficiently well trained that troubles are quickly remedied.'[13]

1942

Lexington was scheduled to receive an FC radar installation similar to *Saratoga*'s, but early war experience led to the removal of her main battery before the FC could be added. Up to her loss at the Battle of the Coral Sea, *Lexington* carried only the CXAM-1 set installed the year before.

Plans for *Saratoga* were revised after her torpedoing in January 1942. The ship immediately returned to Pearl Harbor, where she landed her 8in battery and her FC radars, which she no longer needed. Thus, when she arrived at Puget Sound an inventory of radio equipment showed only the CXAM-1.[14] This condition was soon remedied. The FC radars were replaced by a pair of FD (Mk 4) fire control sets. These were mounted on new Mk 37 DP directors, one each fore and aft in the superstructure. They had essentially the same electronics as the FC; the aerial was basically the same elliptical section as the FC's, except that the two halves were stacked vertically. The aerial was carefully aligned to the optics of the Mk 37. The rapid advances made in the construction and use of radar were such that the ship's comments about the FDs were entirely positive. It was reported to 'be very satisfactory in all respects...and have needed a minimum of repairs – none serious – not affected by gun fire'. A range of 40,000yd was reported for a single aircraft at medium altitude, 30,000yd for an aircraft at low altitude and a cruiser-sized warship and 26,000yd for a destroyer.[15]

Such was the growing reliance on search radar that CNO directed that all major warships were to have a second set in reserve. This new search set, an SC-1, was installed on a small platform on the after lip of the funnel. The radar's electronics were not available for installation during the Puget Sound refit and the set was in fact put in place by the ship's company at sea. The first location tried for the control and display apparatus was on the aft end of the funnel at the second level, immediately forward of No. 3 twin 5in mounting. This was found to be vulnerable to excessive shock when the guns were fired and the electronics were relocated two levels down on the main deck in the passageway outboard of the aftermost uptake. The location of the aerial at the aft lip of the funnel subjected it to continual intense heat, but this seemed to have no serious impact on

the radar's operation. The insulators and oil (in the rotator bearings) had to be checked by the crew every second day; crew members given this unpleasant task had to wear gas masks and could last only about 15 minutes in the heat.[16]

The SC, as its designation implied, was the third in the series of production search radars. It was intended to provide the capability of the CXAM with a much smaller mattress aerial; it could detect a single aircraft at 63nm at high altitude, at 47nm at 3,000ft and at 21nm (42,000yd) at low altitude. An aircraft-carrier, cruiser and destroyer could be detected at 30,000, 25,000 and 18,000yd, respectively.[17] Like the CXAM, the SC-1 had general search capabilities, but such radars were already being seen primarily as air search sets.

A radar set designed specifically for surface search, the SG, was fitted to *Saratoga* at the same time. Operating on a wavelength of 10cm, the SG provided significantly better resolution than *Saratoga*'s other search radars. Its display electronics included a PPI, making it especially useful in giving the ship a clear picture of the surrounding waters.[18] The small, curved aerial was mounted about halfway up the foremast. It could detect an aircraft-carrier at 50,000yd, a cruiser at 47,000yd and a destroyer at 38,000yd.[19] The only problem with the SG was that, because it was not mounted very far up the foremast, the superstructure largely obscured the aft quadrant. The SG was mounted so low on the foremast because the power of the returned signal in early radars was an inverse function of the length of the aerial cable. The longer the cable, the more signals fell below the strength level at which they could be distinguished from noise. This was especially true of the SG, because, in the early days of radar, higher frequency generally meant lower power. The problem was eventually solved by better cable shielding and higher power levels.

January 1944

This radar suite was carried by *Saratoga* without change until she entered the yard at Hunters Point for a refit in January 1944, but shortage of time prevented any major reorganization of the radar. Newer units simply replaced older ones at the same locations. The SC-1 aft was replaced by an SC-3; this had a slightly bigger aerial, giving it improved accuracy, and included PPI presentation. The CXAM-1, now obsolescent, was replaced by an SK, which employed the same electronics as the later SCs, but with an aerial the size of the CXAM's, which gave it excellent performance and accuracy.

Both search radars incorporated BL IFF in their electronics and both aerials included the small narrow rectangular aerial of the BL on top of the radar mattress.[20]

The only addition to the radar fit at this time was the installation of a second SG, actually a somewhat more powerful SG-1, located on a short mast at the after end of the funnel. This was added to provide the coverage of the aft quadrant invisible to the forward SG. (The forward SG had been upgraded to SGa, with the same power as the SG-1, probably sometime during the preceding year.)

A pair of CIC spaces were created on the main deck to house the rapidly multiplying radar and other electronic devices. The larger one served the forward radars and was located in the after half of the captain's cabin; the smaller was aft, directly under No. 3 twin 5in mounting at the aft end of the funnel.[21] Both were considered to be makeshift affairs, like the radar modifications made at this time. A better arrangement would be arrived at when a more lengthy yard period was scheduled.

June 1944

That longer yard period, three months, started on 17 June 1944. It was preceded by several months of discussion about where to locate and how to arrange the permanent main CIC. The primary need was for more room, the temporary one being far too cramped. The original plan was to take over the space occupied by the Photo Lab on the main deck, on the port side aft of the forward elevator, but this was rejected due to the excessive work involved in relocating the lab equipment.[22] Instead, four smaller compartments immediately aft of the temporary main CIC were to be taken over: two staterooms, the coding room and the officers' barbershop.[23] This combined space was not only large enough to hold the CIC, but would accommodate air plot as well.

The revisions made to the radar suite at this time were extensive. The foremast was rebuilt to hold the SK radar which was moved from the funnel. As a result, the forward SGa was deleted and a new SG-1 set was installed at the top of the foremast. The FD radars were upgraded by the addition of a co-axial Mk 22 'orange peel' aerial; this aerial moved independently of the FD in a rocking motion, providing the height-finding capability that the FD lacked. The location previously occupied by the SK was taken over by an SM-1 'pencil beam' fighter control radar. The SM aerial was a 6ft circular

dish which included BM and BO IFF aerials. BN IFF was added to the SG-1s. An SO-11 zenith search radar was to have been installed, but proved to be unavailable.[24]

February 1945

The SC-3 installed in January 1944 was apparently the source of considerable unhappiness in *Saratoga* due to general unreliability and lack of accuracy. The ship asked that it be replaced by an SR radar, a new air search radar then just being released to the fleet.[25] When an SR was found to be unavailable, *Saratoga* then requested an SC-4, similar to the

Below: *Saratoga* received major additions to her radar suite during her early 1942 refit. As well as the CXAM-1 on the funnel, which had been there since late 1941, this view also shows the forward FD on the Mk 37 director and the small SG radar on the foremast platform, 14 May 1942. (NARA)

SC-3 but with anti-jamming circuitry, which was installed during this yard period.[26] Mk 32 IFF equipment for the FD radars was shipped to Puget Sound for installation in *Saratoga*, but it is not clear whether it arrived in time to be installed.[27]

1. Actually, there was a CXAM which preceded the CXAM-1, but differed only in the aerial. In all, 20 CXAM and CXAM-1 sets were produced.
2. BuShips, Sara -> ComAirBatFor, 25 February 1941, Naval Message 252350.
3. BuShips, BuShips -> ComAirBatFor, 1 March 1941, Naval Message 011815.
4. BuShips, 16 June 1942, Interview of Cdr Alfred M. Pride in the Bureau of Aeronautics, p 8. The A type oscilloscope showed range (time) as a scanned horizontal line; any contacts showed as spikes in the scanned line. Range was judged from position on the line, bearing from the position of the aerial. The PPI (Plan Position Indicator) display that is common today, which shows bearing and range in a circular two-dimensional plot, was not introduced until mid-1942.
5. BuShips, Sara -> BuShips, 16 October 1941, RADAR - CXAM-1 Equipment.
6. BuShips, Lex -> BuShips, 7 November 1941, Radar Equipment, effect of turret fire on.
7. BuShips, 16 June 1942, Performance and Operational Report - Radar Equipment: CXAM-1.
8. BuShips, Sara -> CNO, 30 December 1941, *Saratoga* FC Radar Equipment - Report on.
9. BuShips, NYPS -> BuShips, 27 November 1941, Naval Message 270420.
10. BuShips, NYPS -> NYPH, 1 December 1941, USS *Saratoga* (CV3) - FC Radar Antenna Installation - Relocation of Forward 5in A.A. Directors.
11. BuShips, 22 December 1941, U.S.S. *Saratoga* – Gunnery Dept. Order No. 3-41: FC Radar.
12. BuShips, Sara -> CNO, 30 December 1941, *Saratoga* FC Radar Equipment – Report on.
13. ibid.
14. BuShips, NYPS -> BuShips, 20 March 1942, U.S.S. *Saratoga* – Inspection of Radio, Underwater Sound equipment – Arrival Inspection - Report of.
15. BuShips, 16 June 1942, Performance and Operational Report – Radar Equipment: FD.
16. BuShips, 15 August 42, Performance and Operational Report – Radar Equipment: SC-1.
17. BuShips, , 16 June 1942, Performance and Operational Report – Radar Equipment: SC-1.
18. BuShips, 16 June 1942, Performance and Operational Report – Radar Equipment: SG. In relation to the PPI, the report is explicit: '...the value of the P.P.I. cannot be praised too highly'.
19. BuShips, 15 August 1942, Performance and Operational Report - Radar Equipment: SG.
20. BuShips, 8 December 1943, Hunters Point -> ComServPac, Naval Message 072115.
21. BuShips, BuShips -> ComServPac, 12 December 1943, Naval Message 112315.
22. BuShips, ComServPac -> BuShips, 12 June 1944, Naval Message 120223.
23. BuShips, ComServPac -> NYPS, 12 June 1944, U.S.S. *Saratoga* (CV3) - Recommended CIC Installation.
24. BuShips, 8 September 1944, NYPS Departure Report.
25. BuShips, Sara -> ComServPac, 21 March 1945, Naval Message 202147.
26. BuShips, 14 May 1945, NYPS Departure Report.
27. BuShips, BuOrd -> BuShips, 4 May 1945, Radar Equipment Mark 32 Mod 1, Installation of in CV-3.

5.3 Miscellaneous Electronic Equipment

This section covers the other systems that do not fit neatly into the categories of radio and radar. These include a variety of means of sensing or communicating with the world or of combatting the sensor systems used by the enemy.

Direction Finders

Radio direction finding (DF) was a well established means of locating the source of intercepted radio signals by the time the 'Lexingtons' were designed and two DF loops (called radio compasses at the time) were installed, one in a small compartment attached to the foremast just under the main battery director platform and the other forward on the main deck, just aft of the anchor windlass room. There were problems with both installations. The foremast position was of temporary wooden construction and was not weathertight. The wooden construction did not offset the fact that the loop was virtually surrounded by massive metal structures and thus proved impossible to calibrate correctly. The forward position was far better at direction finding because the loop aerial in this case was erected in the centre of the flight deck near the bow. The problem was that the loop had to be dismounted for flying operations, making it unavailable when it was most needed.[1] *Saratoga* had a different use of DF in mind when she complained about the inadequacy of such facilities:

> 'It must be realized that on long-range aircraft scouting problems, it will be extremely difficult for aircraft to correctly navigate back to the carrier, especially during thick weather and where the carrier has made considerable movement during the plane's absence. It seems that radio compass is the most practicable means of accomplishing this problem in navigation; in very thick weather it would be the only means possible.'[2]

For this purpose, multiple DF loops were required. *Saratoga* proposed the installation of two DB receivers and their associated aerials in specially constructed booths at the after corners of the flight deck. Experience with *Langley* had shown that one DF loop at each corner was better, but *Saratoga* could recommend no practical location for permanent loops at the bow. The booths were to be attached to the outside of the flight deck structure, and the loops themselves would protrude outwards from the booths on hinged arms. This recommendation was in fact implemented, the two additional DF sets being added to both ships prior to *Lexington*'s first inspection in 1931. The only deviation from plan was that the DF booths were brought into the main structure of the flight deck, under the ramp in each corner. That inspection showed them to be operating successfully and specifically being used for the purpose of locating returning aircraft. So successful were they at this, at least for aircraft located in the quadrants abaft the beam, that the inspectors recommended the removal of the two forward sets to similar installations near the bow.[3]

Saratoga was scheduled to get upgraded DO sets in 1934, but objected strenuously to the simple replacement of the bow set with a newer model, as the existing set was virtually never available. Instead, *Saratoga* proposed that this set be relocated to a site on the port edge of the main deck near the bow, on a hinged arm much like the aft installations.[4] This was done very much as *Saratoga* requested, the only difference being that it was mounted on a rigid platform close into the hull rather than on a hinged arm. This mounting proved unfortunate as the close proximity of the hull and the steel mesh lifenets just above tended to interfere with accurate readings. However, on the night of 11 February 1935 the loop and its pedestal were carried away in a storm. No attempt was made to restore the mounting in that position and *Saratoga* was left with two DF sets.[5] (Sometime prior to 1934, *Saratoga*'s foremast set had also been deleted.)

In March 1942, arriving at NY Puget Sound for repairs, *Saratoga* now had three sets, two DP-8s mounted in the aft corners and a DP-10 set on the island. During the first of her 1941 refits, this set had been mounted on a housing at the forward lip of the flag bridge, where it stood in the open.[6] The early 1942 refit included extension of the flight deck aft; there was no longer room for the two aft DF sets in the new structure, so one of them was relocated to the superstructure on the aft face of the funnel at the level of the superfiring twin 5in mountings and the other was deleted.[7] *Saratoga* fought most of the war with these two DF sets, but apparently all DF gear was removed at about the time that RCM gear was installed, at the beginning of 1945.

Sound Equipment

As designed, the 'Lexingtons' were intended to receive underwater listening equipment (sonar), both active and passive. The plans were made despite a ruling from CinCUS that capital ships were not to be fitted with sonar.[8] Despite these instructions, plans had apparently proceeded to the point that BuCon recommended that the installation in *Lexington*, which was further advanced at the time, be completed and that in *Saratoga* be deferred.[9] CNO agreed with this plan, which would allow tests be made with *Lexington* and ascertain whether the installation in *Saratoga* and other capital ships was justified.[10] Therefore, a JB sound receiver and a KC sound transmitter (which together formed a system known as an MV compensator) were installed in *Lexington*. Actually, the original plans called for two transmitting units, but during the lengthy debate over this installation, one had been diverted to other construction and the decision was made to

Left: Close-up of the front of the forward Mk 37 director with its FD radar, *Saratoga*, 14 May 1942. Note that the radar and the visual rangefinder arms could be cross-levelled - i.e., they would keep to a true level with the horizon while the ship pitched or rolled. This explains the odd angle assumed by both in this view. This photo was taken to show possible interference between the upper hatches on the Mk 37 and the FD aerial when the ship rolled. (NARA)

Right: A view from *Saratoga*'s foremast platform down into Sky Forward, showing the rear of the Mk 37 director and FD radar, 14 May 1942. (NHC)

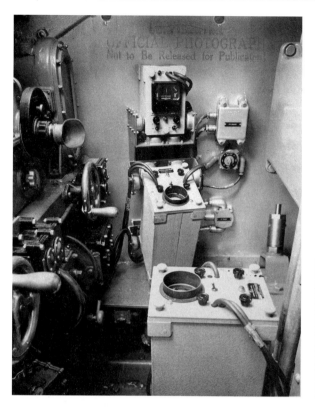

Left: During *Saratoga*'s major refit in the autumn of 1944, SM pencil-beam radar was installed on the forward funnel platform and the SK search radar, which had replaced the CXAM earlier in the year, was moved to a platform on the foremast, 6 September 1944. The 'bow and arrow' aerial at the top of the foremast is for the YE aircraft beacon. Also visible is a 'ski pole' IFF aerial on the signal yard. (NARA)

Far left: The inside of the forward Mk 37 director on *Saratoga*, 14 May 1942. The controls on the left are for the visual rangefinder integral with the director. The electronics to the right control the FD radar. (NARA)

Left: The aft end of *Saratoga*'s funnel, 14 May 1942, showing the SC-1 aerial on its platform at the after lip of the funnel and the aft Mk 37 with its FD. (NARA)

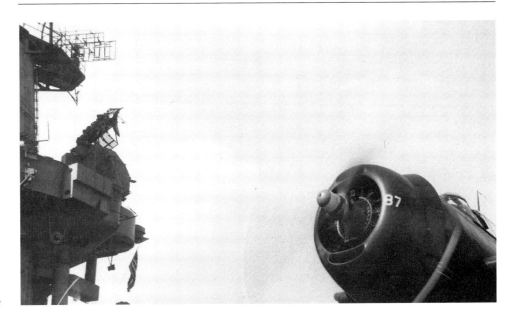

Right:: This view of *Saratoga*'s aft superstructure, dated 4 February 1945, shows the Mk 22 'orange peel' aerial added to the Mk 37 director coaxial with the FD and the SC-3 aerial, which replaced the SC-1 on the aft lip of the funnel. (NARA)

Right:: This post-war view of *Saratoga*, taken at Alameda, CA, on 27 February 1946, shows the final state of her radar suite, with an SC-4 replacing the SC-3, the aft SG-1 on its stub mast to the left of the SC and the forward SG-1 at the top of the foremast. YJ-1 aerials are just visible on either side of the forward SG. (NARA

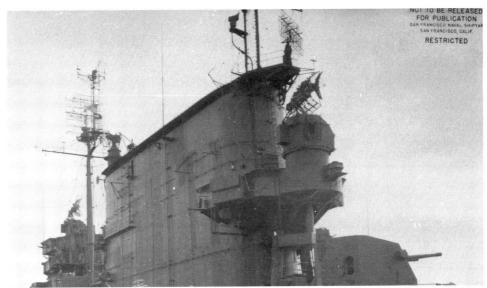

complete *Lexington* with just one unit.[11] (Both ships also received separate NC fathometer systems for depth soundings.) *Lexington*'s experiments with the sound equipment were far from successful and the ship asked for the removal of the equipment:

> 'Repeated attempts have been made to take bearing of sound by the compensator. Interference from the many ship noises makes this impracticable. The compensator has for the last year been used only for reception of the incoming signal in taking "deep" sounding with the fathometer.'[12]

Despite this report, the unit not removed from *Lexington* and correspondence dating from 1934 shows that BuEng was planning to replace *Lexington*'s sonar with a newer unit:

> 'While it is realized that vessels of the "Lexington" class have little if any need of elaborate sound equipment for the detection or tracking of other vessels, it is felt that some means should be provided for listening to lightship bells and oscillators and for use in radio-sound distance finding when more synchronized lightship stations are installed in the United States.'[13]

In 1935 both ships received upgrades to their fathometer equipment, getting NM-1a units in place of the old NC units. *Saratoga* replaced this unit in 1944 with a complete NMB-1 sonar unit, but obviously not for the purpose of underwater search.[14] No mention can be found of *Lexington*'s sonar after 1934, indicating that it fell into disuse.

Other Devices

Radio Counter-measures (RCM) – now an aspect of today's ECM – was in its infancy during the Second World War. Basically, the options available at that time included detection of enemy radio or radar activity, which potentially could warn of an attack, and active jamming of enemy wavelengths, potentially nullifying the enemy's attempts at search and communications. By late in the war, US Navy vessels, including *Saratoga*, were carrying more and more sophisticated RCM gear.

There is little evidence of RCM equipment on *Saratoga* before the beginning of 1945, when the Departure Report submitted by NY Pearl Harbor on 10 January mentions the installation of unspecified 'RCM radar' projecting from the SM radar platform on the forward lip of the funnel.[15] Obviously other equipment was installed then or earlier, because photographs of *Saratoga*'s island structure taken after the 21 February 1945 Kamikaze attack show a pair of combined AS-56/AS-57 aerials (collectively known as SPR-1) projecting from either side of the forward DF position at flag bridge level. SPR-1 (also known by its USAAF designation APR-1) was a passive collection system designed to detect Japanese radars. The report of the repairs done after that attack mentions the replacement of power cables to an SPT-4 transmitter located on the forward edge of the funnel. SPT-4 was an active jammer which operated in the range of 200-550MHz and was derived directly from the APQ-2 airborne jammer, designed for use in strategic bombers against night fighter radars. *Saratoga* requested the replacement of her SPT-4 jammer with the newer and more powerful TDY-1a, which operated in the higher frequency S band, but the request was turned down because this system required a pair of jamming aerials mounted near the waterline. Aircraft-carriers were not generally given the TDY-1a because it was difficult to find locations for the aerials and because it was primarily intended as a counter-measure against enemy shipborne fire control radars, not against airborne threats.[16]

Before and during the Kamikaze attack on 21 February 1945, *Saratoga* maintained RCM watch, using the SPR-1, in the 70-300MHz range, because that was the known frequency range of Japanese airborne radar. No interceptions were made before the attack, indicating that the Kamikazes found *Saratoga* without the aid of radar. The SPR-1 set was also used earlier in the day to monitor a change being made to the frequency of the after FD radar. The change was made in an attempt to separate more widely the frequencies of the two FDs, making the pair more difficult to jam by a single jammer.[17] This was an early example of the kind of electronic warfare strategy, of deception and

Left: Controlling the multiple radars and understanding the picture they created required the creation of a CIC. *Saratoga*'s main CIC was moved and expanded during her autumn 1944 refit. This photo, dated 6 September 1944, shows the forward end of the CIC with two FDO positions, left and right, with their SK radar repeaters (canvas covered in this view), and the large plotting screen in the middle. (NARA)

Left: The SM radar console on the port side of *Saratoga*'s CIC, 6 September 1944. (NARA)

Below: The aft DF 'loops' on the 'Lexingtons' were mounted on pivoting arms extending from the ramp of the flight deck. This is the port mounting on *Saratoga*, 18 October 1932. (NARA)

counter-deception, that is common today.

The final item of 'communications equipment' of interest was one that was proposed but never actually fitted to the 'Lexingtons':

'Up to the time the *Langley* was commissioned, every naval air station had carrier pigeons. We used to take these on flights. Before you started your flight, you went over to the pigeon loft and got your little box with four pigeons in it...Then, if you had a forced landing, of which we had quite a number, you wrote your message...and stuck it in the capsule that was fastened to the pigeon's leg and let it go. It flew back to the air station, and they knew where you were presumably.'

Langley was launched with a pigeon coop right aft.

'We went into Chesapeake Bay and anchored off Tangier Island to shake down. The pigeon quartermaster - there was such a fellow - would let his pigeons out, one or two at a time, for exercise. They'd leave the ship and fly around, and they usually stayed in sight. Pretty soon they'd come back and land.'

The idea worked fine for a while, then disaster struck:

'The assistant flight officer, Lt Cdr Griffin, said to the pigeon quartermaster, "Let them all go". The pigeon quartermaster demurred a little. But the commander said, "Go ahead, let them all go."

'So the pigeon quartermaster opened the coop and let all the pigeons out at once. They

took off just like that, heading for Norfolk. They had been trained while the ship was in the Norfolk Navy Yard...

'That was the last we saw of pigeons on the *Langley*. So they made the pigeon coop into the executive officer's cabin, a very nice one incidentally.'

This turn of events directly affected the design of the 'Lexingtons':

'There were nice compartments up on the main deck...that were assigned as pigeon lofts, and one in each ship-big compartments...

'I'd hardly reported when we saw those. They'd make fine berthing compartments. So we got the pigeon lofts deleted from the plans of the *Lexington* and *Saratoga* and made them into berthing compartments. That's a little absurd, but that was one of the things we did.'[18]

1. I&S, Report of Material Inspection of U.S.S. *Lexington* (CV2) Held 27, 28 and 29 October 1931, p 74-5.
2. BuCon, PCO Sara -> BuCon, 30 October 1926, *Saratoga* - Radio Telegraph; recommendation for immediate construction of two additional compass booths for use with aircraft.
3. op. cit., p 74-5.
4. BuCon, Sara -> BuEng, 24 July 1934, Radio; Direction Finder Location - recommendation for.
5. BuCon, Sara -> BuEng, 25 March 1935, Model DO-1 Direction Finder; operating tests of and damage to, report of.
6. BuShips, NYPS -> BuShips, 20 March 1942, U.S.S. *Saratoga* -Inspection of Radio, Underwater Sound equipment - Arrival Inspection - Report of.
7. BuShips, NYPS -> BuShips, 2 June 1942, U.S.S. *Saratoga* - Inspection of Radio, Underwater Sound equipment – Departure Inspection – Report of.
8. BuCon, Superintending Constructor, Quincy -> Inspector of Machinery, Quincy, 5 August 1926, Underwater Sound – U.S.S. *Lexington* – Installation of 18 spot underwater sound receiver on.
9. BuCon, BuEng -> CNO, 17 December 1926, Underwater Sound – U.S.S. *Saratoga* and U.S.S. *Lexington* 18-spot sound receivers and sound transmitters.
10. BuCon, CNO -> BuEng, 28 December 1926, U.S.S. *Saratoga* and U.S.S. *Lexington* 18-spot Sound Receivers and Sound Transmitters.
11. BuCon, BuEng -> BuCon, 10 February 1927, Underwater Sound – U.S.S. *Lexington* - Underwater Sound Transmitting Equipment.
12. BuCon, Lex -> BuCon, 31 July 1931, MV Compensator – Request for removal of.
13. BuCon, BuEng -> CNO, 5 September 1934, Underwater Sound -U.S.S. *Lexington* - Removal of 18-spot Sound Receiving Equipment.
14. BuShips, 8 September 1944, NYPS Departure Report.
15. BuShips, 10 January 1945, NYPH Departure Report.
16. BuShips, Sara -> BuShips, 8 March 1945, U.S.S. *Saratoga* (CV3) – Alteration Request No. 58-45. BuShips' denial of the request was in its endorsement dated 19 March 1945.
17. BuShips, Sara -> CinCUS, 26 February 1945, U.S.S. *Saratoga* (CV3) Action Report for period 0900 (K) to 2130 (K), 21 February 1945 - Forwarding of.
18. Oral, Pride Interview No. 2, p 56-8

Left: *Saratoga*, after the Kamikaze attack off Iwo Jima, 22 February 1945. As well as the wrecked crane and the burnt-out Hellcat, this view shows some of the interesting electronics installed in US ships late in the war. A pair of SPR-1 passive RCM aerials project from the front of the island at flag bridge level. A pair of 2AX-NAN 'Nancy' IR beacons can be seen on either side of the foremast just below the SK radar platform at the top of this view. (NARA)

Below: Another post-war view of *Saratoga*, 27 February 1946, showing an array of aerials at the base of the SM radar platform at the forward edge of the funnel. The 'stovepipe' aerial to the left was for the BM IFF system; the four circular plates arrayed around the platform were aerials for the SPT-4 active jamming system. (NARA)

Postscript

The 'Lexingtons' were pioneers throughout their careers. It is appropriate that their deaths should be as momentous as their lives. *Lexington* was lost at the Battle of the Coral Sea on 8 May 1942, the first fleet carrier to sink in the first purely naval air battle. *Saratoga*'s death came in peacetime, but was every bit as historic. She was one of the target ships anchored in the lagoon at Bikini atoll for the US Navy's tests of the atomic bomb in Operation 'Crossroads'. As a result of the second of these tests, on 25 July 1946, *Saratoga* received damage sufficient to cause her to take on water aft. Since the target ships were unmanned, no damage control measures could be taken and the flooding increased until, that same day, she slipped stern first beneath the waters of the lagoon.

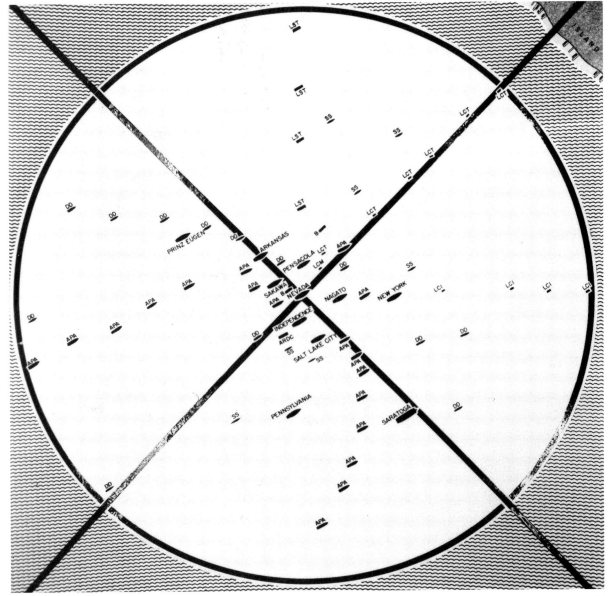

Left: *Saratoga* still intact after 'Able Test', 11 July 1946. Because she was relatively undamaged in the first blast, she was apparently moved closer to ground zero for the second test. (NARA)

Below: Observers watch 'Baker Test', 25 July 1946, from what was thought to be a safe distance. (NARA)

Bottom: *Saratoga* sinking not long after the 'Baker' blast, 25 July 1946. Most of her funnel has been blown over, leaving just the aft uptake standing. The battleship *New York* (BB34) is in the background to the right. (NARA)

Glossary

AA   Anti-aircraft gun
ADM   Admiral
avgas   aviation gasoline (petrol)
BB   Battleship
Brig Gen   Brigadier General. Equivalent to Brigadier in British usage
BuAer   Bureau of Aeronautics
BuCon   Bureau of Construction & Repair
BuEng   Bureau of Engineering
BuOrd   Bureau of Ordnance
BuShips   Bureau of Ships
CAG   Commander Air Group
CAP   Combat Air Patrol, a defensive patrol around the aircraft-carrier by its fighter aircraft
CAPT   Captain. Highest non-flag rank in the USN. Also the normal title for any CO of a USN ship, regardless of rank
CDR   Commander
chow   Slang for food
CIC   Combat Information Centre
CinC   Commander-in-Chief
CinCPac   Commander-in-Chief, Pacific Fleet
CinCUS   Commander-in-Chief, US Fleet
CNO   Chief of Naval Operations. Operational commander of the US Navy
CO   Commanding Officer; or, in the section on the inert gas system, carbon monoxide
CPO   Chief Petty Officer. A senior non-commissioned officer
ComAirBatFor   Commander Aircraft, Battle Force
ComAirPac   Commander Aircraft, Pacific Fleet. Successor to ComAirBatFor
ComServPac   Commander, Service Force, US Pacific Fleet. Responsible for all forward maintenance and repair of ships in the Pacific
CV   Aircraft-carrier
DD   Destroyer
DF   Direction Finder
DP   Dual- Purpose. A term used to describe a weapon usable against both air and surface targets
ENS   Ensign. Equivalent to RN Sub-Lieutenant
FY   Fiscal Year. The budgetary year covered by government appropriations. At this time, the fiscal year began on 1 July of the preceding calendar year
GE   General Electric Corporation
gedunk   soda fountain
GQ   General Quarters – the highest crew readiness state
head   water closet
HE   High-Explosive
HF   High-Frequency, between 3-30MHz
IC   Internal Communications, or intercom
IFF   Identification Friend or Foe
JO   Junior Officer
kHz   Kilohertz. The WWII equivalent was Kilocycles (kcs)
LCDR   Lieutenant Commander
Lex   *Lexington*
LSO   Landing Signals Officer
LT   Lieutenant
LTJG   Lieutenant Junior Grade
MAA   Master-at-Arms
Mae West   An inflatable life vest of rubberized canvas, yellow in colour
MHz   Megahertz. The WWII equivalent was Megacycles (Mcs)
Mod   Model. In US military nomenclature, when a mark of an item was modified, it was given a one-up mod number (the basic mark being considered Mod 0)
mg   machine-gun
MIT   Massachusetts Institute of Technology
MF   Medium-Frequency, between 300-3,000kHz
Mk   Mark. In US military nomenclature, completely new versions of a particular item were given successive mark numbers, as in the Mk 4 fire control radar
Ms   Measure
n/a   Not available or not applicable
NAS   Naval Air Station
nm   nautical mile
NRL   Naval Research Laboratory
NY   Navy Yard
NYPH   Navy Yard Pearl Harbor
NYPS   Navy Yard Puget Sound – the main West Coast navy yard
OOD   Officer of the Deck
OpNav   Office of Naval Operations. CNO's staff office

PCO	Prospective Commanding Officer	sonar	sound navigation and ranging. The USN term for ASDIC
pdr	pounder. Refers to the weight of a shell fired from a gun	STS	Special Treatment Steel. A hardened steel often used as backing for or as replacement for armour. Each 10lb of basic weight translates into $1/4$-in thickness
PO	Petty Officer		
Pri-Fly	Primary flight control station		
RADM	Rear Admiral. This rank in the USN actually covers the two lowest flag ranks; RN equivalents are Rear Admiral and Commodore		
		TBS	Talk Between Ships. A VHF radio system designed for local communication
RCA	Radio Corporation of America		
RCM	Radio counter-measures; now a part of ECM	UHF	Ultra High Frequency, between 300-3,000MHz
RF	Radio Frequency	UNREP	underway replenishment
RN	Royal Navy	USN	United States Navy
rpg	rounds per gun	VHF	Very High Frequency, between 30-300MHz
Sara	*Saratoga*		
scuttlebutt	water fountain. By connotation, the gossip that spread among the crew while hanging around the water fountain	VF	Carrier Fighter Aircraft
		VSB	Carrier Scout Bomber
		VT	Carrier Torpedo Aircraft
		WO	Warrant Officer
ShipAlt	Ship Alteration Request	XO	Executive Officer
shp	shaft horsepower		

Paint Schemes

For most of their careers, the 'Lexingtons' were painted standard navy grey, a very light neutral colour. This was the US Navy's normal peacetime paint scheme both before the Second World War and since. This colour was applied to all vertical surfaces from the waterline upwards. Decks were a variety of colours before the war. The flight deck was painted maroon with orange striping to facilitate aircraft operations.[1] Where external decks were steel, they were painted dark grey; where they were linoleum, they were left unpainted, allowing the colour of the linoleum (generally brown) to show. The waterline was painted black with a boot-topping mixture (Formula No. 3A). Below the waterline, the hulls were painted with an anti-corrosive (Formula No. 42B) and then covered with a coat of anti-fouling mixture (Formula No. 142).[2]

The two 'Lexingtons' were so similar in appearance that their first air groups complained that they were impossible to distinguish from the air. Soon after their entry into the fleet, the carriers were each given a black stripe on the funnel: horizontal on *Lexington* and vertical on *Saratoga*. The ships also painted their nicknames in large letters on their flight deck aft. Otherwise, the 'Lexingtons' carried few visible markings. The US Navy awarded prizes to ships in the fleet which exhibited excellence in some aspect of shiphandling. Ships which earned the award for engineering (steaming) could paint a large white 'E' on their funnel. *Saratoga* carried such a marking in 1936-37 and *Lexington* in 1938. For a while in 1934 *Saratoga* painted a crest in white on her funnel stripe, but this had disappeared by 1935.

As war approached, the US Navy adopted camouflage schemes. Both 'Lexingtons' were painted in Measure 1 (Ms 1), dark grey on all vertical surfaces up to the level of the funnel tops. Anything above that level was painted light grey. These greys were still neutral in tone. *Lexington* was given a further touch: Ms 5, which was a false bow wave painted in white. The flight decks were stained dark blue with a specially concocted wood stain soon after the beginning of the war. *Enterprise* had apparently experimented with a prussian blue stain just before the war and ComAirBatFor had ordered

all Pacific Fleet carriers to use *Enterprise*'s formula. But when *Lexington* tried to requisition a three-month supply of prussian blue pigment in November 1941, a long delay ensued, after which she was informed that this pigment was a war critical material and she should use the deck blue stain manufactured at Mare Island.[3]

Photographs of *Lexington* taken while she was having her main battery removed in March 1942 show her in what might be Ms 12, a graded camouflage system introduced in September 1941. This scheme, when applied to aircraft-carriers, comprised sea blue (5-S) up to the level of the hangar deck and ocean grey (5-O) from there up the top of the superstructure. These were new colours, based on a purple-blue tinting material used in various amounts and mixed into a white base. Sea blue was a medium blue-grey made with one part tint to four parts base. Ocean grey was a lighter grey made with one part tint to eight parts base. These photographs of *Lexington* show her in what appears to be the process of being repainted, while the few unclear photos of her later at the Battle of the Coral Sea appear to show her in a single-tone camouflage. If that was indeed the case, then the photographs of *Lexington* at Pearl Harbor in March 1942 probably show her being painted in Ms 11, overall sea blue. This is the same scheme in which *Saratoga* was painted when she emerged from the navy yard at Puget Sound in May 1942.

Saratoga remained painted in Ms 11 only until she was torpedoed again in August 1942. When her repairs were complete, *Saratoga* was painted in the new Ms 21, overall navy blue (5-N). This was darker than sea blue and was made out of three parts tint to eight parts base. This scheme, as with the earlier Ms 11, was intended to be effective against aerial observation. Apparently by the autumn of 1944 the threat from the air in the Pacific had diminished to the point that *Saratoga*, when she emerged from her refit in September, was given a new camouflage designed to be effective against surface and sub-surface observers. She was painted in a boldly patterned disruptive scheme, Ms 32/11-A.[4] This consisted of irregular patches of three colours: light grey (5-L), ocean grey and dull black (BK).

Left: *Saratoga* would have been impossible to distinguish from *Lexington* at any distance were it not for the vertical funnel stripe. When this photograph was taken, on 31 May 1934, *Saratoga* had a circular crest painted on her funnel stripe. (NARA)

Left: In 1935 *Lexington* received AA platforms at each bow and quarter and around her funnel. This photo dated 28 April 1938 shows these platforms and an 'E' for excellence on her funnel. By that time she had also had her flight deck widened forward. (NARA)

Light grey was a very pale colour in the same tinted series, using one part tint to 40 parts base; dull black was a true black with very low reflectivity. This scheme was supposed to confuse the close observer as to the true identity and bearing of the target. At a distance the three colours blended into a medium grey.

The Navy was wrong in its belief that the air threat had disappeared: the emergence of the Kamikaze made that threat greater than ever before. *Saratoga* was to become a victim of such an attack off Iwo Jima in February 1945. Before she sailed to that battle, she was repainted in Ms

21, which scheme she wore for the rest of her life.

1. I&S, Report of Material Inspection of U.S.S. *Lexington* (CV2) Held 27, 28 and 29 October 1931, p 13.
2. I&S, 5 September 1941, U.S.S. *Lexington* (CV2) – Material Inspection of.
3. BuShips, Lex -> BuShips, 4 February 1942, Naval Message 311920.
   BuShips, BuShips -> Lex, 11 February 1942, Naval Message 101515.
4. BuShips, NYPS -> BuShips, 21 October 1944, U.S.S. *Saratoga* (CV3) – Photographs, Completion with Report of Camouflage.

Above: Painting ship was a constant preoccupation of the bosun's force. To get under the overhang at the bow, as here on *Lexington*, 12 February 1930, required ropes, booms and considerable acrobatic skill. (NARA)

Above right: An overhead shot of *Saratoga* on 11 December 1936, showing her nickname now painted on the aft end of the flight deck and an 'E' award on her funnel stripe. (NARA)

Right: As well as the funnel stripes, the 'Lexingtons' had their nicknames 'Lex' and 'Sara' painted on the flight deck to remind pilots which carrier they were approaching. This photo shows *Saratoga* on 7 November 1931, with her name painted on the ramp. (NARA)

Above: *Lexington* was painted in the earliest of US Navy camouflage schemes, as seen here on 14 October 1941. This is Ms 1, overall dark grey, with Ms 5, a white false bow wave. (NARA)

Left: *Lexington* at the time her main battery was removed at Pearl Harbor, 31 March 1942, in what appears to be an attempt at Ms 12, a graded system; although it might be Ms 11, overall sea blue. (NARA)

Left: *Saratoga* in the Solomons in August 1942, not long before being torpedoed for the second time. She is painted in Ms 11, overall sea blue. When she returned to combat early in 1943, it was with Ms 21, overall navy blue. (NARA)

Right: Murderer's Row, early version! This name was later given to the line-up of fast fleet carriers that would assemble at fleet anchorages such as Majuro or Ulithi between strikes. This early gathering was seen at Majuro on 2 May 1944. The carriers, all painted in Ms 21, near to far, are *Saratoga*, the new *Yorktown* (CV10) and *Enterprise* (CV6). In the far distance to the left are the battleship *Iowa* (BB61) and another battleship, probably *New Jersey* (BB62). (NARA)

Right and below right: Two photographs showing both sides of *Saratoga*'s complex Ms 32/11-A, which she carried only briefly, starting in September 1944. The colours were light grey, ocean grey and dull black. (NARA)

Right: When *Saratoga* returned to combat in early 1945, she was again wearing Ms 21, as here two days after the Kamikaze attack that put her out of the war, 23 February 1945. Note the hole punched in her stability bulge by one the attackers, just under the pair of 40mm guntubs in her starboard boat pocket. (NARA)

Left: An interesting decoration in an unlikely spot. *Saratoga* had this map of the Pacific theatre painted on the forward bulkhead of her hangar; the Solomons can be seen behind the distinguished speakers addressing the crew on the occasion of her 16th birthday, 15 November 1943. From the left, the speakers are: Rear Admiral Frederick C. Sherman, who commanded *Lexington* at the Coral Sea battle, Admiral William Halsey and Captain J.H. Cassady, *Saratoga's* CO. (NARA)

Left: An interesting feature can be seen in this photo of deck crews fighting the fires on 21 February 1945. *Saratoga* had the outline of a false lift pJainted on her flight deck forward of her two real ones. There is no way of knowing whether this influenced the aim of the Kamikazes, but all seemed to hit in the vicinity of the false lift. (NARA)

Air Groups

Organization

Between the wars each squadron of US Navy aircraft was an independent entity. Carrier squadrons were organized into air groups, which in turn were assigned to aircraft-carriers. However, they were viewed as simply operating from the ship on a nominally temporary basis, even though a single air group would, particularly in peacetime, operate from the same ship for many years. During the war, when combat losses and the increased operational attrition due to intensified training could decimate an air group in months, the turn-over was much faster.

Each squadron was an autonomous unit, complete not only with aircraft and pilots but with maintenance personnel and spare parts inventories as well. When a squadron was assigned to shore duty, even temporarily, it took not only its aircraft ashore but also all its support staff and their impedimenta.[1] Even if a squadron was to be ashore only for the few days its carrier was in port, it would need its complete staff if it intended to do any flying before the

ship sailed again. In theory, at least, one air group could be replaced by another in a matter of hours.[2]

Squadron size varied considerably over time, but a look at a 1941 fighter squadron illustrates the relative numbers and roles of assigned personnel. This squadron would have a nominal establishment of eighteen aircraft and at least as many officer/pilots to fly them.[3] As well as flying the aircraft, the officers of a squadron had additional command or administrative responsibilities. The squadron was led, on ship and in the air, by its commanding officer, usually a lieutenant-commander. He was assisted by an executive officer, responsible for handling the daily problems of the squadron, and a flight officer, who handled flight scheduling, aircraft assignment and the training of junior pilots. These three officers each led a division of six aircraft in the air. Other officers led the engineering, gunnery, communications, materiel and personnel divisions. The 120 enlisted men who did the work of maintenance and preparation on ship were divided among those divisions. These included line chiefs, plane captains in charge of the maintenance of individual aircraft and the aviation mechanics, metalsmiths and radiomen who did the work.[4] They also included non-aviation ratings such as pharmacist's mate, storekeeper, cook and baker, making the squadron truly independent of the ship.

The outbreak of war forced a change in the practice of moving a squadron's enlisted personnel ashore whenever the squadron flew off:

> 'In peacetime the carrier air group can bounce ashore with everybody, stay there, and be shore-based for a long time; then on a scheduled date embark with all their spares. Now, of course, that's utterly impossible. The carrier group comes ashore when the carrier gets into port, or just before it does, and it's got to be ready to go to sea at any time, and the carrier's got to be ready to operate a group at any time.
>
> 'Carrier Aircraft Service Units...have been built up because of that. When the carrier comes ashore they've tried to fix the framework of a group ashore. They can't bring the carrier personnel ashore because they

Below: Leaning on the railing outside Air Plot on second level of the bridge structure, Lieutenant Commander J.C. 'Jumping Joe' Clifton, CO of VF-12 (centre), discusses the weather with CAG-12, Commander Howard H. Caldwell (right) during support for the invasion of the Gilbert Islands, 30 November 1943.

can't embark 'em fast enough if they have to sail in a hurry. Particularly when you have to send a group to, say, Kaneohe and the carrier is at Pearl Harbor....So they've organized a combined pool of men - just as if you'd combined all four squadrons. They have people who are specifically qualified in fighters, scout bombers, torpedo-bombers. And it's working out very well.

'The one thing the Carrier Aircraft Service Units suffer from is lack of spares. It throws a tremendous strain on the whole supply situation in aviation, because they have to have spares and the ship itself has to have spares. However, the ship can cut down on its spares some, and it has.'[5]

With the coming of war and the establishment of permanent CASUs at all naval air stations, squadron support personnel became a more integral part of the aircraft-carrier, leaving the ship only when the squadron was permanently reassigned.

Each air group was led by a Commander, Air Group (CAG). On ship, the squadrons' COs, and ultimately CAG, were responsible for the readiness of the air group. In the air, CAG had total responsibility for his squadrons. But he had no say, officially, over when his aircraft were launched, how many were launched and what the mission would be. That was the job of the ship's air department and the air officer. These in turn took their direction from the ship's captain and the task group commander. The interests of the ship's air department and the squadrons often came into conflict. It was the job of CAG and the air officer to work out problems before they got out of hand. One point of contention was training. The squadrons wanted to maximize flying time when not in actual combat in order to keep the pilots well trained; the ship's air department often saw this as a nuisance, since part of its job was to keep an effective defensive patrol in the air. Sometimes there was friction:

'The *Lexington* was a ship administered in every way to enhance the value of the air group. The training of the air group at sea in gunnery and bombing was given high priority. This condition did not exist on all our carriers; some of the carrier commanding officers apparently still did not consider the air group the main battery. In addition, certain restrictions were placed on the carrier commanding officers. As an example, the restriction on practising in fighter interception. We couldn't open up on the radio at all.'[6]

Even if the air group was given adequate opportunities for training, problems could still arise in practice:

'Yes. There is training. They go out and fire whenever they get an opportunity. They comb slicks whenever they get a chance. But they can't bring the sleeves back to the ship. They've tried it. Jimmy Thach went to the mat about it and finally sold me on the idea and I went to the Admiral and the Captain and sold them on the idea and Jimmy picked his prize pilot and he came back and dropped a sleeve aboard – young Guyler – who, incidentally has five "Japannies" to his credit – and he damn near won a Japanese decoration that day. He fixed up five SBDs. He came in too low, didn't release the sleeve in time, and the sleeve caught on one and the line swept along up the deck and there were five SBDs thrown out of commission....And when you can't get your sleeve back you've lost a lot of the value of fixed gunnery.'[7]

Above: *Lexington*'s flight deck with aircraft from at least three of her squadrons, 26 January 1929. In the foreground are Boeing F3B-1s of VF-3B; note the '3-F-5' marking on the side of the aircraft at lower left, indicating that this is the fifth aircraft in Fighting 3. Just behind are F3B-1s and Curtiss F6C-3s of VB-1B, formerly VF-5S. The direction of the upper wing chevron marking distinguishes some of the aircraft of these two squadrons. In the background, parked over the arrester wires, are the big Martin T4M-1 torpedo-bombers of VT-1B.

Above: The CO's aircraft of VF-6B in full regalia at the Cleveland Air Races, 1 August 1934. A Boeing F4B-4, it was painted aluminium overall, but there were so many markings and stripes that the base colour barely showed. The vertical and horizontal tail surfaces are white, indicating that this machine came from *Saratoga*. The upper wing surface is chrome yellow for visibility at sea. The cowling, wing chevron and fuselage stripe are red; the colour denoted the first section of the squadron, and the fuselage stripe and fully painted cowling denoted a section leader. Lettering was black, except where it ran over the fuselage band, where it was white. The tail markings gave the serial number on the fin and the aircraft model on the rudder. The squadron insignia, also black, was 'Felix the Cat'. The F4B-4 was one of the most popular aircraft flown by the Navy. Navy fighter squadrons often sent detachments to such popular events as air races to put on dramatic dogfighting and dive-bombing displays.

In some ships, squadron officers had shipboard responsibilities when they were not flying. Before the war, for example, pilots in *Lexington*'s air group were required to stand periodic bridge watches.[8]

Composition

Each air group was intended to include all the types of aircraft that the ship would need for offensive and defensive combat. From the beginning, the composition of the 'Lexingtons'' air groups varied constantly, both in terms of aircraft types and numbers and actual aircraft models, as experience and the rapid evolution of aviation technology offered better options. When the 'Lexingtons' were nearing completion, thought had to be given to their employment and to the composition of their air groups:

> '*Lexington* will be a unit of the Scouting Fleet and will carry on board: 2 VF squadrons of 27 planes each (18 operating, 9 reserve); 2 VT squadrons of 24 planes each (16 operating, 8 reserve); and half a VO squadron, the other half of which will be on the battleships of the Scouting Fleet. (This squadron will consist of 12 operating and 6 reserve.)
>
> 'In addition to the above, there will be a Utility squadron of 3 planes, type VO, and probably odd planes for test purposes, for radio liaison, and other incidental work, probably not amounting to more than 4 or 6 planes.'[9]

The basic types of aircraft to be used and the

tactics to be employed had been developed through the pioneering work done with *Langley* since the latter had come into service in 1923. The US Navy designated all heavier-than-aircraft types with a 'V' prefix followed by one or more letters indicating function: e.g., VF (fighter), VT (torpedo-bomber) and VO (observation aircraft). The basic roles assigned to these aircraft were offensive and defensive interception for the VFs and torpedo attack for the VTs. Initially the VFs were expected to double as light, low-altitude bombers and the VTs as heavier, high-altitude bombers.[10] VOs were scout aircraft, equipped optionally with wheels or floats. By mid-1929 *Saratoga*'s air group (or CVG) comprised:

> VF-1B equipped with 22 Boeing F2B-1s and one Vought FU-2
> VB-2B equipped with 15 Boeing F3B-1s and one Vought FU-2
> VS-2B equipped with five Vought O2U-1s and five O2U-2s and
> VT-2B equipped with 19 Martin T4M-1s.[11]

Squadron designations were made up of the aircraft type, followed by a hyphen, then a sequence number and a fleet assignment suffix. Thus VF-1B was the first fighter squadron (Fighting One) and was assigned to the Battle Fleet (hence the final 'B'). The designation VS indicated a scouting squadron, the successor to the planned VO squadron, although the equipment type and mission had not changed. Aircraft designations were type indicator (one or more letters), sequence number (by manufacturer), manufacturer's code letter, a hyphen and the version number. Thus the F2B-1 was the first version of the second fighter type produced by Boeing for the US Navy. At that time there were no specialized dive-bombing aircraft and VB-2B, for example, was equipped with fighters.[12]

On 1 July 1937 a Fleet Squadron Reorganization was authorized in an attempt to rationalize the designations of squadrons and air groups. CVGs were given the same number as the hull number of the aircraft-carrier to which they were assigned. Thus the *Saratoga* Air Group became CVG-3 and *Lexington*'s Air Group CVG-2. All squadrons assigned took the CVG number. Thus CVG-3 at the end of 1937 comprised:

VF-3 (formerly VF-6B) equipped with 18 Grumman F3F-1s and one Curtiss SBC-3
VB-3 (formerly VB-2B) equipped with 18 Vought SB2U-1s
VS-3 (formerly VS-2B) equipped with 18 Curtiss SBC-3s
VT-3 (formerly VT-2B) equipped with 18 Douglas TBD-1s.[13]

New aircraft type indicators show up in the model designations of the aircraft that made up CVG-3. There were now SBC-3s and SB2U-1s,

which were scout bombers (i.e., purpose-built dive-bombers which doubled as scouting aircraft), and TBD-1s, which were torpedo-bombers (i.e., torpedo aircraft equipped to act as level bombers).[14] In addition, *Saratoga* carried the following aircraft not assigned to CVG-3: two Grumman J2F-1s and three Vought O3U-3s assigned to the ship's utility squadron, and one Grumman F3F-1 and two Vought SBU-1s reserved for flag use.[15]

The coming of war caused a rapid evolution in all aspects of a CVG. From the beginning, the pressure grew to increase the number of fighters at the expense of other aircraft types, as it soon became apparent that splitting a fighter squadron so that some fighters accompanied a strike, some remained at home flying CAP (Combat Air Patrol) and some stayed on deck in reserve meant there were too few to perform adequately any of these roles. *Saratoga*'s CO, after the initial Solomons operations in August 1942, concluded:

'In the opinion of the Commanding Officer, the outstanding lesson of the entire operation was the pressing need for a greater number of shipborne VF type airplanes and their ready availability to Commander Aircraft. In a large complement of mixed types such as was embarked in the *Saratoga* flexibility in the use of fighters is seriously compromised. While it is generally accepted that the fleet fighter is

Right: The fighter component of CVG-12, three-colour Grumman F6F-3 Hellcats of VF-12, warming up prior to launch off *Saratoga*, 20 November 1943. The Grumman TBF-1 Avengers of VT-12 behind and the Douglas SBD-5 Dauntlesses of VB-12 at the rear await their turn. The Hellcats are painted in two shades of non-specular blue with white on the undersurfaces. Their only markings were the blue and white national insignia and the white aircraft number on the fuselage side.

Below: Vought SB2U-1s of VB-3 on *Saratoga*'s deck, 8 February 1938. Their colourful markings would disappear just before Pearl Harbor.

each quarter of SBDs, to assist in shooting down those torpedo planes because the fighters can't be everywhere and those planes are positioned – they're not under fighter direction, they're simply positioned to stop that attack at the last, if they can.'[17]

In practice the tactic worked only moderately well. At Coral Sea, *Yorktown* (CV5) put up a low CAP of nine SBDs, of which four were lost early in the battle to a trio of Zeros escorting the attacking torpedo-bombers, with no Japanese loss in return. *Lexington* had fifteen SBDs as close-in CAP, nine from VS-2 to port and six from VB-2 to starboard. They were flying at 2,000ft about 3,000yards from the ship. VS-2's Dauntlesses managed to down three Japanese torpedo-bombers during their run in on *Lexington*; during the retreat of the Japanese air groups, a VB-2 SBD shot down a dive-bomber, but during this phase lost one of their own, as did VS-2. Thus, in total, the SBDs lost six against four enemy aircraft shot down.[18]

The obvious answer was more fighters and the size of fighter squadrons did in fact grow steadily. By the end of 1943 *Saratoga*'s air group comprised: VF-12 equipped with 37 Grumman F6F-3 Hellcats, VB-12 with 24 Douglas SBD-5 Dauntlesses, and VT-12 with 18 Grumman TBF-1 Avengers.[19] Note the disappearance of a distinct VS squadron. The distinction between the roles of the VS and VB squadrons had begun to blur in the late 1930s with the development of the hybrid scout-bomber, most notably the SBD Dauntless. Equipped with the same aircraft, either squadron could be assigned the other's duties.[20] The emergence of the TBF as the standard torpedo-bomber – a large long-range machine – gave the carrier air group another aircraft with natural search capability. It was a logical step, then, simply to absorb the VS into the VB and increase the size of the VB by a third. This had the additional advantage of allowing the VF squadron to be increased dramatically in size. Note also that *Saratoga* was operating CVG-12, not CVG-3. Any attempt to maintain the match of air groups with hulls was quickly overwhelmed by the needs of war. It was far easier to replace an aircraft-carrier's air group than to work new pilots and aircraft models into an existing group, and during the war *Saratoga* was 'home' to at least four different air groups: CVG-3, CVG-12, CVG-53(N) and CVG-8. The third of these, as indicated by the 'N' suffix, marked the change of role for *Saratoga* into a night-duty carrier.

In 1944 the increasing threat of night attack

primarily a defensive weapon, its potent contribution to the offensive effort as escort for dive-bombers and particularly torpedo planes leads to the conclusion that serious consideration should be given to equipping such vessels as the new converted Cleveland type with fighters only.'[16]

To relieve, at least partially, the pressure on the fighters until larger squadrons could be formed, it became standard practice to augment a high-altitude CAP of fighters (which protected against dive-bomber attack) with a low-altitude CAP of scout bombers (specifically Douglas SBD Dauntlesses, which mounted a pair of forward-firing .50cal machine-guns) protecting against torpedo attack. The biggest fear was of a co-ordinated sequential attack by dive-bombers and torpedo aircraft that would draw the CAP up or down and leave the other path unguarded – exactly what the Americans did to the Japanese at Midway.

'Well, they're using bombers for fighters. When a torpedo attack is imminent they'll put a sort of a Lufberry circle on each bow and on

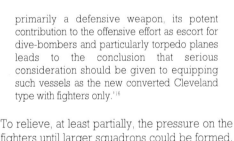

Left: One SBD-5 Dauntless is dragged forward while another traps on *Saratoga*, April 1944. The colours are the same three tones of blue and white; the aircraft's number is repeated small on the tail. The two stripes aided the LSO in lining the aircraft up during approach; if he could see one stripe but not both over the wing, the aircraft had the correct approach angle. Note that the national insignia is all white, the blue being omitted.

Left: CAG-53's aircraft, an F6F-5N Hellcat night-fighter, is towed aft on *Saratoga*, 4 February 1945. CAG aircraft were often marked '00' (known as 'double nuts'). Note the leading-edge radar aerial fairing. Aircraft are now painted overall glossy sea blue.

Left: C-8By 1945 there were so many CVGs flying similar-looking aircraft that unit markings became necessary. The white chevron on the tail and the starboard wingtip marked the aircraft of CVG-53, one of which burns while two more F6F-5Ns await a launch that never happened at the beginning of the Kamikaze raid on *Saratoga*, 21 February 1945.

on its carrier task groups led the US Navy to switch its two oldest operational carriers, *Saratoga* and *Enterprise*, to the role of night-duty carrier. CVG-53(N)'s nominal establishment at the end of 1944 was: VFN-53 with 57 F6F-5 and F6F-5N Hellcats, and VTN-53 with 18 TBM-3D Avengers. The F6F-5N differed from the standard F6F-5 primarily in mounting an AN/APS-6 radar aerial in a fairing projecting from the leading-edge of the starboard wing.

During the war, in addition to the regular air groups, a few unusual aircraft occupied *Saratoga*'s flight deck. Arriving back at Pearl Harbor just too late to take part in the Battle of Midway, *Saratoga* was assigned to carry two squadrons of aircraft to reinforce the decimated defences of that island: one was a squadron of Marine SBD Dauntlesses, while the other was the USAAF's 73rd FS, 18th FG, with 25 Curtiss P-40 fighters. These occupied the very aft end of the flight deck, where they would have the maximum take-off run. No one in the USAAF squadron had tried flying off a carrier before; nevertheless, the launch was made without incident on 17 June 1942 approximately 200 miles east of Midway Island.[21] On at least one occasion, a Royal Navy aircraft landed and took off from *Saratoga*'s deck. On 16 May 1944 Rear Admiral Moody, commanding the aircraft-carrier element of combined TF66 operating in the Indian Ocean, flew aboard *Saratoga* for a planning session in a Fleet Air Arm Fairey Barracuda.

1. This organization was due in part to the fact that most aircraft in the early days of aviation were produced in very small numbers, often only enough to equip a squadron or two, and a replacement squadron stood a good chance of flying a different aircraft.
2. Symbolic of the detached relationship of air groups from their carriers is the fact that an aircraft-carrier's machines normally fly off the ship as it approaches port and do not rejoin again until it is back at sea. One practical reason for this is that when a ship is in port for an extended period, it is impossible for pilots to maintain a training regime from a moored flight deck.
3. Most of the information in this paragraph is derived from 1st, p6-7. Before the war, squadrons were assigned more pilots than aircraft because that would allow the squadron to launch all aircraft even if a pilot or two were sick or injured.
4. In non-fighter squadrons which flew multi-seat aircraft, these aviation ratings also manned the rear seat, The Hook, Fall 1978, p4.
5. BuShips, 4 June 1942, Interview of Cdr C.R. Brown, Air Officer, U.S.S. *Saratoga* in the Bureau of Aeronautics.
6. BuShips, 26 August 1942, Interview of Lt Cdr John S. Thach in the Bureau of Aeronautics. Thach was probably referring to *Enterprise* (CV6), which at the time had a reputation for feuding between the air department and the air group, cf., 1st, p58 & 60.
7. op.cit. The pilot referred to by Cdr Brown was Lt Noel A.M.

Gayler, flight officer of VF-3. In Brown's defence, his name was pronounced as if it were spelled 'Guyler', cf., Gates, Thomas F., Felix the Cat, Part Two – Felix Goes to War in the Hook, Fall 1980, p11.
8. Hook, Fall 1979, p7. This was from an article by Max Schwartz entitled Service in USS *Langley* (CV-1) 1930-31.
9. BuCon, BuAer -> DirBudget, Past, 1 April 1927, Present, and Future Mission of the Carrier *Langley*; also contemplated use of the *Lexington* and *Saratoga*.
10. Almost from the beginning, fighter aircraft were used in the light bombing role. Since the performance of these early fighters suffered terribly as soon as bombs were hung from their wings, their pilots did not relish the low-altitude bomber role, feeling that their chances of falling victim to defensive fire were excessive. During the 1920s they evolved dive-bombing tactics to increase accuracy and survivability. This role became so important that on 1 July 1928, *Lexington*'s VF-5S was redesignated VB-1B and *Saratoga*'s VF-6B was redesignated VB-2B.
11. Data from a chart developed by William T. Larkins and reproduced in Tailhook Update No. 4, Summer 1981. *Lexington*'s air group was similarly organized and equipped.
12. In 1930 the two squadrons which had been designated VBs (cf., footnote 10) reverted to their original VF designations although their missions and equipment remained the same. VBs would not reappear until 1934.
13. BuCon, Sara -> BuCon, 17 December 1937, U.S.S. *Saratoga* (CV3) - Displacement and Battle Waterline. The numbers reported in this document represent the nominal establishment of the squadrons; reality was often different. In mid-1938, Larkins shows VF-3 with 16 F3F-1s, 2 O3U-3s (utility squadron aircraft?) and 1 SBC-3; VB-3 with 21 SB2U-1s, 1 XSBA-1 and 1 N2Y-1 (a trainer); VS-3 with 21 SBC-3s and VT-3 with 21 TBD-1s.
14. Just to keep things confusing, the US Navy would drop the manufacturer's sequence number for the first aircraft of a type made by a manufacturer. Thus the TBD-1 was the first version of the first torpedo-bomber made by Douglas.
15. op.cit.
16. BuShips, Sara -> CinCPacFlt, 19 August 1942, Report of Action Tulagi - Guadalcanal Offensive 7-8 August, 1942. Captain Ramsey was referring to the 'Independence'-class light aircraft-carriers (CVLs) then being converted from 'Cleveland'-class light cruisers. In a few cases the first CVLs did see action in 1943 with an all-fighter air group, but it became standard practice to equip them with a large fighter squadron and a small torpedo-bomber squadron. For example, CVG-23 on *Princeton* (CVL23) in late 1943 was composed of VF-23 (24 F6Fs) and VT-23 (9 TBFs).
17. BuShips, , 4 June 1942, Interview of Cdr C.R. Brown, Air Officer, U.S.S. *Saratoga* in the Bureau of Aeronautics.
18. BuShips, , 17 June 1942, Interview of Lt N.A. Gayler in the Bureau of Aeronautics. However, the bulk of the information in this paragraph is extracted from the detailed coverage of the air combat during the Battle of the Coral Sea in 1st.
19. Colour, p160.
20. Nowhere was this more evident than, when the VF, VB and VT squadrons of *Saratoga*'s air group were transferred to *Yorktown* for the Battle of Midway, the sole *Yorktown* squadron that remained onboard, VB-5, changed its designation to VS-5 to avoid the confusion of having two VBs in the same air group.
21. This was not the first time that USAAF P-40s had flown off an aircraft-carrier. On 10 May 1942, 40 P-40s had flown off *Ranger* for Accra, Gold Coast (now Ghana), en route to India.

References

Primary Sources

The information in this book is based almost entirely on the study of primary sources. Fortunately for this historian, the 'Lexingtons' served in a navy on the winning side in the Second World War; there is no dearth of documentary material readily available on the development and operation of *Lexington* and *Saratoga*. If anything, so much material exists that the historian is faced with a major job in sifting through the mountains of available documents. Sources used by the author included:

CNO Inspection & Survey Reports. Held at NARA, Washington, DC, in RG 38.

Correspondence (General & Classified), General Board of the Navy. Held at NARA, Washington, DC, in RG 80.

Correspondence (General & Classified), Bureau of Construction & Repair. Held at NARA, Washington, DC, in RG 19. Material from 1915-1925 is in Entry 105; material from 1925-1940 is in Entry 115.

Correspondence (General & Classified), Bureau of Ships. Held at NARA, Suitland, MD, in RG 19.

Correspondence (Secret & Confidential), Secretary of the Navy. Held at NARA, Washington, DC, in RG 80. This material has been microfilmed and has a separate index.

Records Relating to US Navy Fleet Problems I to XXII, 1923-1941. Held at NARA, Washington, DC, primarily in RG 38. This material has been microfilmed and has a separate index.

The Oral History Collection of the US Naval Institute also proved invaluable. The author was able to make use of two transcripts, those of Admiral Alfred M. Pride and Rear Admiral Ernest M. Eller.

Secondary Sources

Books

Breyer, Siegfried, *Battleships and Battle Cruisers, 1905-1970*, Doubleday & Co., Garden City, NY, 1973. First published as *Schlachtschiffe und Schlachtkreuzer 1905-1970* by J.F. Lehmanns Verlag, Munich, Germany

Friedman, Norman, *Naval Radar*, Naval Institute Press, Annapolis, MD, 1981. First published in Great Britain by Conway Maritime Press

Friedman, Norman, *U.S. Aircraft Carriers: An Illustrated Design History*, Naval Institute Press, Annapolis, MD, 1983. The definitive design history of the US Navy's aircraft-carriers

Kilgrain, Bill C., *Color Schemes and Markings U.S. Navy Aircraft 1911–1950*, self-published, Victoria, BC, Canada, 1973

Johnson, Stanley, *Queen of the Flat-Tops*, Dell Publishing Co., New York, NY, 1942. A first-hand account of the loss of *Lexington* by a contemporary war correspondent

Lundstrom, John B., *The First Team*, Naval Institute Press, Annapolis, MD, 1984

Melhorn, Charles M., *Two-Block Fox*, Naval Institute Press, Annapolis, MD, 1974

Sowinski, Larry and Tom Walkowiak, *United States Navy Camouflage of the WW2 Era*, The Floating Drydock, Philadelphia, PA, 1976

Sowinski, Larry and Tom Walkowiak, *United States Navy Camouflage of the WW2 Era: 2*, The Floating Drydock, Philadelphia, PA, 1977

Terzibaschitsch, Stefan, *Aircraft Carriers of the US Navy*, Naval Institute Press, Annapolis, MD, 1980. First published as Flugzeugträger der US Navy. Band 1: Flottenflugzeugträger by Bernard & Graefe Verlag

Periodicals

The Hook, Bonita, CA. The quarterly journal of the Tailhook Society, an organization conceived to promote the US naval air community

The US Naval Institute Proceedings, Annapolis, MD. The monthly journal of the US Naval Institute, a private organization supporting the interests of the US Navy

Warship International, Toledo, OH. The quarterly journal of the International Naval Research Organization, an association of naval historians and those interested in naval history

Naval History, Annapolis, MD. A relatively new quarterly journal published by the US Naval Institute

Index